Otto Lowenstein was born in Munich in 1906. He graduated from the University there with a First in Natural Sciences and went on to obtain his D. Phil. in 1932. In 1933 he became a displaced scholar and moved to Birmingham where he was able to continue his work with the aid of a grant from the Academic Assistance Council. In 1937 he went to Exeter as Assistant Lecturer and in 1938 to Glasgow, where he held a lectureship until he returned to Birmingham in 1952 on his appointment to the Chair of Zoology and Comparative Physiology.

Professor Lowenstein was elected to the Fellowship of the Royal Society of Edinburgh in 1946 and to that of London in 1955. He has published papers in scientific journals and is currently President of the Institute of Biology. Apart from science, his interests lie in the fields of philosophy, music, and painting.

Otto Lowenstein

THE SENSES

PENGUIN BOOKS
BALTIMORE · MARYLAND

Penguin Books Ltd, Harmondsworth, Middlesex, England
Penguin Books Inc., 3300 Clipper Mill Road, Baltimore 11, Md, U.S.A.
Penguin Books Pty Ltd, Ringwood, Victoria, Australia

—

First published 1966

—

Copyright © Otto Lowenstein, 1966

—

Made and printed in Great Britain
by Richard Clay (The Chaucer Press) Ltd,
Bungay, Suffolk
Set in Monotype Plantin

CONTENTS

CONTENTS

CONTENTS

PREFACE

THIS book is addressed to the interested layman and to the young professional biologist. It is not a textbook; it can best be described as a series of essays. These have their origin in academic teaching. They are condensed, selective, and do not aim at completeness, nor in every instance is there any intention to give chapter and verse for assertions made and inferences drawn. With a few exceptions, all that is here presented is owed to the work of others. They will have to be content to see the results of their labours, the triumphs of their discoveries, make their contributions to a remarkable story that could not have been written were it not for their ingenuity. Sometimes only when a discovery of fundamental importance demands acknowledgement will specific reference be made to the discoverer. A short list of useful reference works is appended to guide the reader to further reading.

The book is selective. This is as it should be in a book of essays, and if I were to have succeeded in whetting an appetite for more I should be well content. It will be seen that, as with all books on science, more often than not the emphasis is on ignorance rather than on established knowledge. Doubt is the mainspring of scientific discovery, and these pages are full of it. They may also contain inaccuracies that cannot with the best of intentions be pardoned in the name of popularization. Scientific information dates rapidly, and it is only too easy to back the loser in choosing between rival hypotheses. Technical terms have been avoided as far as is possible, and I have tried to explain the unavoidable ones on first presentation.

Most of the text figures are sketches, very much like blackboard drawings made to help the student visualize what is being talked about. The structures depicted are rendered over a wide range of reductions and magnifications without indication of scale. The omission of scales is deliberate. They would only convey a false impression of accuracy. Some of the representations of electron-microscopic findings are based on overall magnifications up to 38,000 times, but, again, scales are not given, because the distortion in the relative size of component structures, introduced for the sake of descriptive emphasis, would render an overall scale misleading.

Naturally, most of the illustrations are more or less vaguely based on original illustrations of other authors. Yet acknowledgement is made only where the figure is a direct and fairly accurate copy of such an original. In most cases the degree of simplification and adaptation, as well as the sketchy rendering, makes it unwarranted to blame the author of the original for the imperfection of the adaptation.

The table of contents, with its many sub-headings, as well as the size of the book make a subject index unnecessary. A list of articles and books for further reading is appended.

INTRODUCTION

What is meant by information in biology

THE idea that the physical universe and the living organisms inhabiting it are two separate and essentially different forms of existence is obsolete. It derives from primitive mythology and implies a house–tenant relationship between environment and living beings. In actual fact non-living objects, such as galaxies, stars, planets, oceans, continents on the one hand, and living organisms on the other, follow each other in their appearance in time during the course of cosmic evolutionary change and are all closely interconnected assemblies of matter and energy. Matter and energy in their turn are freely interconvertible. Nothing, therefore, in the whole universe exists in isolation.

When living organisms gradually evolved from non-living matter, they began to differ from it by their increasing complexity and of course by being capable of self-reproduction. However, they remained purely material systems through which passes a constant flow of materials coming from the inorganic environment and returning to it. In fact, when we analyse the fine structure of a plant or an animal, we find it hard to draw the borderline between living and non-living constituents. This is an intriguingly fascinating problem, but it is not part of our story.

The maintenance of the living state depends on a great number of complex chemical processes. Most of these are controlled by the collaboration of intricately interlocked systems of enzymes, and these in turn depend for their proper functioning on temperature and on the relative constancy of the concentration of key substances in and around living cells. Organisms show an astonishing resistance to change, and this is brought about by self-regulatory mechanisms. Human techno-logists have throughout the ages either consciously or more often unconsciously copied these in the design of machines. Modern automation – however incredible some of its achieve-ments – is a mere trifle as compared to what happens in the self-maintenance, growth, and reproduction of a plant or an animal.

It is convenient to define the difference between plant and animal by saying that animals, thanks to their greater mobility, have acquired a greater degree of independence of their environment. They have, however, lost the power to live on simple inorganic raw materials such as carbon dioxide, water, and certain simple salts. They can evade the conse-quences of rapid changes in their environment and they can select an environment which offers most suitable conditions for successful survival. Food-gathering, the pursuit of animal prey, the defence against predators, mate selection, the selective establishment of associations with other organisms in symbio-sis, in parasitism, or in all manners of social relationship – all these are dependent on the continuous gathering of informa-tion about what happens in the environment. There is a con-stant need for rapid changes in the whole organism's activities, with all the necessary adjustments in the coordination of body and limbs.

It is necessary here to say a word or two about what is meant by information. In recent years scientists and technologists have made this common word of our everyday language into a well-defined technical term, especially in the field of com-munications engineering. They speak of so many 'bits' of in-formation passing along a telephone wire or over a radio or television carrier wave. We are at this moment not interested in this specific meaning of the term 'bit' and especially not in its quantitative aspects, nor in information theory in general. If I inform my neighbour by telephone that, in his absence, his house has caught fire, I am sure to bring about a significant change in his state of mind, which in turn is bound to influence his immediate actions. Not all information need be as dramatic as this. A deer 'getting wind' of an intruder into its territory receives through the intruder's scent information of his approach. A blind man tapping his stick on the pavement seeks to obtain information about the number of doorways he passes by assessing by ear the nature of the echo. A sheep-tick locates a suitable warm-blooded host by delicately sensing the rise in air temperature in its immediate neighbourhood. A navigator on the bridge of a ship searches the horizon for a tiny spot of flickering light from the beacon marking a dangerous rock. A spider becomes alerted to the presence of a struggling prey caught in the meshes of its web by the mechanical vibration of a specific signalling thread which it keeps 'in touch with' while waiting in its lair. Even a plant sends its shoot upward and drives its root down into the soil by sensing the direction of gravity in a way not yet completely understood.

This is what I mean when, as a biologist, I stress the importance of continuous utilization by organisms of information about environmental conditions. Changes in the environmental situation may either come about by actual changes in the physical or chemical conditions near the organism, or by the organism moving from one place to another. In order to cope with such changes the animal has to gather information continuously and react to it rapidly. This means that the organism must be closely 'tuned in' to its surroundings and be capable of receiving a wide range of different stimuli.

Sense organs as pathways of information

The organs concerned with this vital function are the sense organs or sensory receptors, and, to use Thomas Hobbes's way of putting it, 'There is no conception in a man's mind, which hath not at first, totally, or by parts, been begotten upon the organs of sense.' We shall have an opportunity later to discuss the philosophical implications of sensory function. Here and now we want to inquire into the biological aspects of this matter. We have first-hand conscious experience of what our eyes, ears, fingertips, nose, and tongue mean to us. Blind people and deaf-mutes have tried to convey to us the contents of their restricted worlds, and we have the case of Helen Keller who, having lost sight and hearing in early childhood, proved nevertheless educable to such an extent that she obtained a college degree and lived a full cultured life. All this she owed to her fingertips and her heightened sensibility, combined with strength of character. The fortunate normally sensed person naturally takes it for granted to reach far into the distance by eye and ear – so much so that he tends rather to neglect the mass of information available to the tactile sense and to nose and palate. For civilized man smell and taste have become faculties almost entirely restricted to the pleasures of the table, while fellow animals depend on the sense of smell at any rate for their safety and orientation in a hostile or friendly world, as the case may be.

In a study of sense organs and their function we find it both convenient and fruitful to start with a survey of sensory experience both introspective and communicated by fellow human beings, who act as observers under controlled experimental conditions. This can serve as a source of knowledge from which we can launch out on our expeditions into the unknown field of sensory mechanism. Of course, it is far more ambitious to try to gain an insight into sensory mechanisms in our fellow animals, and this can only be achieved by the use of objective methods. Similarly, even in ourselves, there are many sensory processes that cannot be studied by means of introspection or with the aid of a human guinea-pig, simply because they never enter the field of conscious experience. One of the senses that hardly ever produces a conscious sensation is the sense of balance. Part of our inner ear is not at all concerned with hearing; its job is to signal to the central nervous system the position of our head in space. It senses how far the head has deviated from its normal position. In this way movements can be accurately controlled if they are active, or compensated for if they are passive – as, for instance, when we stumble.

Talking about stumbling: we regain our balance and bring body and head back on to an even keel by quick balancing movements of our arms and legs, but if these are to be smooth and effective, we need yet another unconscious sensory process. The very muscles of our limbs and body are themselves liberally supplied with sensory structures: they are stimulated by the changes in tensions which accompany contraction and relaxation of the muscles.

The joints of our limbs, too, abound with 'sensory probes' which tell us, at any given moment, the accurate position of our limbs relative to the body. We can, in absolute darkness, find the tip of our nose with the tip of a finger. We couldn't do that unless we had sensory outposts in our joints and skin. We know we can do it, but we don't consciously experience how it's done. It's no wonder that this very important sensory mechanism remained rather unexplored and badly understood until quite recently, and much of what we now know about it we have learnt from experiments on animals in which reactions to sensory stimuli were accurately observed, measured and analysed.

The nature of sensory stimuli

What are sensory stimuli? In more general terms any fairly rapid change in the physical or chemical make-up of the organism's environment can act as a stimulus, provided the organism is attuned to it by the possession of a selectively sensitive nervous structure that can translate a physical environmental change into a coded 'sensory message', to be conveyed from the receptor site to the central computing house of the central nervous system.

A new way of classifying sensory receptors

We can subdivide sensory stimuli into three categories with regard to their physical nature: namely, into mechanical, electromagnetic, and chemical stimuli. Light and radiant heat are electromagnetic cosmic phenomena of fundamental importance for the self-maintenance of living organisms. They also play an important role as carriers of vital information in the organism's orientation in its environment.

Sight, the first and foremost of the classical 'five senses', is fairly universally found in the animal kingdom, where eyes of varying complexity serve in the perception of the visible part of the electromagnetic spectrum. We shall deal with this in detail in the next chapters, where we shall find that it constitutes only a very small part of the total spectrum of electromagnetic energy, and where we shall investigate the question of what other parts of this spectrum might conceivably play a part in orientation.

The sense of touch and pain as well as the great variety of sensory mechanisms for the control of posture, movement, balance, and, finally, for hearing depend on the registration of mechanical deformation of parts of the body situated at the surface or in deeper tissues and in special sense organs. As heat is physically speaking a mechanical phenomenon, the temperature sense, too, will have to be dealt with under this heading. It will be seen that the organs of the temperature sense are in fact closely allied to the organs of touch.

Smell and taste are the chief chemical senses, but, as can be expected, animals react to a wider range of chemical agents than those familiar to us through the good offices of our noses and palates, and it will be necessary to consider a general chemical sense in addition to the two classical categories of smell and taste.

We may say, therefore, that instead of the old five senses based on human conscious experience, we shall be dealing with three classes of sensory function. They cover together a range of different sensory modalities wider than that encompassed by the classical five senses.

The coding and the transmission of sensory information from sense organs to central nervous system

The sense organs are the outposts for the reception of sensory stimulation, or, as an engineer would say, the inputs through which sensory information passes into the organism. How do they select the appropriate information and in what form do they hand it on to the rest of the nervous system, especially to the brain? We have seen that the physical nature of stimuli

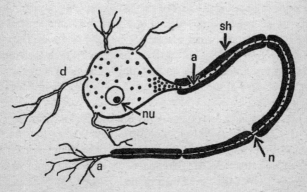

Figure 1. This shows a neuron with its cell body and typical nucleus (nu), its dendrites (d), and axon (a). The axon is insulated by the fatty sheath (sh) which is divided into segments by nodes of Ranvier (n). The axon is not represented at its proper length in proportion to the size of the cell body. Axons of microscopically small neurons can be many feet long.

differs widely. Yet when we study what goes on in the sensory nerves on stimulation of a sense organ, we find that, irrespective of the type of sense organ and the nature of the stimulus, all sensory nerves carry signals of monotonous uniformity.

Nerves can to a certain extent be likened to electric cables. They consist often of a great number of conducting fibres corresponding to the individual insulated wires of a compound cable. They, too, are generally well insulated by fatty sheaths which are wound tightly around them and are derived from special so-called glia cells which make up an important part of all nervous tissues. Inside its insulating sheath a nerve fibre consists of a living membrane and a core of cytoplasm. It is the process of a nerve cell or neuron (Figure 1). In ourselves and all backboned animals the cell bodies of the sensory neurons are sometimes found collected together in bodies of nervous tissue known as ganglia. The sensory ganglia either make up part of the brain or lie in pairs on either side of the spinal cord, one pair per segment along part of the backbone. They send a long process to the receptor site at the periphery and a shorter one into the spinal cord where it 'synapses' or makes contact with the general network of nerve processes which distribute the sensory information up and down the cord and to the higher centres of the brain. We shall deal with this in detail in Chapter 10.

For the conduction of nervous information the membrane of the nerve fibre is the important part. Across it we find established and maintained by the metabolic living activity of the nerve cell an electric potential of about one-tenth of a volt. The outside of the nerve membrane is positive and the inside negative. The potential is the result of the active maintenance of a delicate equilibrium in the concentration outside and inside the nerve fibre of potassium, sodium, and chloride ions in a manner that cannot be dealt with here in detail. The analysis of this process and of the generation of the nerve impulse is one of the great stories of twentieth-century biological discovery, in which British biophysicists and physiologists such as the recent Nobel Laureates, Hodgkin and Huxley, have taken a leading part.

A nerve impulse occurs whenever the resting potential across the nerve membrane is sufficiently disturbed by outside influences that interfere with the resistance and capacity of the membrane. The membrane can become, so to speak, depolarized, which means that the resting potential can be reduced or obviated by mechanical deformation, by chemicals, by heat or even by light, and of course by the action of outside electric potentials applied to it. When the depolarization has gone far enough an 'explosive' event can take place which consists in the rapid reversal of polarity. The outside of the fibre becomes negative to the inside. This process can take place within less than a thousandth part of a second and is reversible. This means that within this time a certain point on the nerve fibre changes from positive to negative and back to positive with the re-establishment of the resting potential. This rhythmical self-reversing change in electric potential is the nerve impulse. It is a disturbance of a balanced state and travels like the ripple on a calm pond from the point of disturbance in all directions. The ripples on a pond caused by a stone breaking its surface die down as they travel outwards. Not so the nerve impulse. On its way along the fibre in both directions from the point of depolarization the disturbance is fed by the energy which maintains an equal resting potential all along the nerve, and the impulses therefore remain of the same magnitude over the whole length of nerve fibre. Moreover, no sooner has one impulse travelled away than a new one can be fired off by a new disturbance or by the continuation of the original one. Impulses can, therefore, follow each other at intervals measured in thousandths of a second or, in other words, at a frequency of up to some hundreds per second. How many impulses per second result from the stimulation of the ending of a sensory nerve depends on the degree of disturbance or, in technical terms, on the extent of depolarization below a critical firing level. This relationship between the intensity of the stimulus and the impulse frequency of the sensory nerve signal was first established by Lord Adrian, another of our British Nobel Laureates.

For our understanding of the process of conversion of stimulus into a nerve signal it is sufficient to remember that stimuli of any kind are ultimately transformed or transduced into series of equal-strength nerve impulses, the frequency of which is a function of stimulus intensity. We shall have to get interested in the problems of stimulus transduction when we deal with the way in which the receptor structures in the various sense organs function. One may say now that the sensory nerve hands on the information received from the environment via the sense organ in the form of a message, which is coded in the form of electrical pulses of variable frequencies.

If the frequency denotes intensity, as Adrian has taught us, then how and where is the information about the physical nature of the stimulus encoded and conveyed to the central nervous system? The answer to this question is at first sight surprising, but becomes self-evident on closer consideration. It is that there is, as a rule, no such thing as a quality code. Whether a flash of light, or the intrusion of a hard crumb into a hollow tooth, or the sound of a telephone bell, or the odour of appetizing food, or a pull on one of the muscles or tendons of a limb, the message invariably consists of a series of electric pulses of a certain frequency, and nothing more. Our recognition of the modality of the stimulus and its quality is determined by the nature of the sense organ which is being selectively affected by the stimulus, and also by the final destination of the nervous message in the central nervous system. It has been suggested that, if it were possible to graft the nerve leading from the eye on to the central portion of the ear nerve and vice versa, and if the nerves healed satisfactorily together, we should *hear* the flash of light and *see* the report of a pistol shot. Conversely, and this can be more easily demonstrated, if you compress your eyeball by a blow on the eye, you see the proverbial stars, just as any interference with the inner ear gives rise either to vertigo (feeling of unbalance) or illusions of sound.

One more point may be made clear by way of introduction. We have seen that the electric potential changes involved in the generation and conduction of the nerve impulse are of the magnitude of one-tenth part of a volt. An electric torch may be operated by a battery of, say, three volts, so the nerve impulse therefore operates at the thirtieth part of the voltage used in the electric torch. Consequently, the currents circulating in the nerve fibre are also minute. And yet we shall see that measurements of the minimum amount of energy necessary just to stimulate the retina of an eye or the receptor of the inner ear, or the sense endings at the tip of a finger, show that these so-called threshold energies are many powers of ten lower in absolute energy units than the energy of the nerve signal resulting from such minimal stimuli. The sensory nerve and its endings in a sense organ must therefore have the power of amplifying the effect of stimulation. How and where this amplification takes place in the various sense organs is another problem with which the student of sensory function has to grapple. Naturally, the very fact of the almost incredible sensitivity of sensory receptors makes necessary the provision of protection against over-stimulation and consequent damage. We shall find that the function of quite a number of the so-called ancillary components of complex sense organs such as the eye or ear is the delicate adjustment or matching of the strength of the incoming stimulus to the range of sensitivity of the receptor endings.

1

LIGHT AND THE LIVING
ORGANISM

The electromagnetic spectrum

WHAT is light? This appears on the face of it to be a straight-forward question. However, questions probing into the actual nature of things of everyday experience can rarely be answered straightforwardly. Light, as we experience it, is the effect on us of a small part of a continuous range of electromagnetic cosmic events. These electromagnetic waves can also be described in an alternative way as streams of particles of energy or energy quanta. They are, like all waves, alternating to and fro. Their rhythm is expressed as their frequency in terms of so and so many times per second. They travel at different speeds through differently dense media, and for a certain frequency their wavelength depends on the speed of propagation. In empty space all electromagnetic waves travel at a speed of 185,000 miles or 300,000 km. per second. This is popularly known as the speed of light. $L = c/n$ is the equation which relates wavelength (L), propagation speed (c) and frequency (n). The wavelengths of visible light range between 390 and 700 millimicrons. A millimicron * $(m\mu)$ is a millionth part of a millimetre. A millimetre in turn is the thousandth part of a metre or a twenty-fourth part of an inch. The wavelength of light is thus very short. The frequency of oscillation is consequently very high. For instance, green light of a wavelength of 500 $m\mu$ oscillates 600,000 million times per second. One may ask what it is that oscillates in a light beam

---

* By international agreement this unit is now called a nanometre, but we are going to use the more familiar old term here.

traversing empty space, and one is in for a rather disappointing answer. The old 'ether' which was assumed to be the massless carrier of such oscillation, as water is a carrier for the ocean waves and air for sound, is an obsolete model-concept. Modern quantum-mechanics have made it possible to build the wave nature of electromagnetic radiation into a scheme

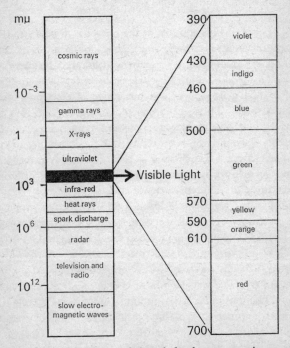

Figure 2. This is a lay-out of the whole electromagnetic spectrum. It illustrates what an insignificantly small portion of it is represented by visible light. This portion is given on the right, spread out to show the correspondence between wavelength and visible hue. The unit chosen is the millimicron (mμ), which is used in the section on colour vision (p. 73), and the spectrum is calibrated in powers of ten of a mμ. (*Modified after Brett.*)

which operates with the fiction of quasi-corpuscles of energy, so-called quanta of discrete energy content. Their energy content depends on the oscillatory frequency of the material source, e.g. of a body of glowing matter. How this model is connected with the behaviour of electrons in their orbits around atomic nuclei is a fascinating chapter in theoretical physics, which we cannot pursue any farther here.

Let us, therefore, be content to use the wave and the quantum model of light, as it suits us best in any given situation, with the comfortable knowledge at the back of our minds that somewhere there exists a set of equations to bridge the conceptual gap.

It is, however, interesting to see how visible light fits into the general electromagnetic spectrum. If we choose 1 mμ, the average wavelength of X-rays, as our unit, we can descend from them via the shortest rays of radioactivity to cosmic rays that may be 100 million times shorter. We can, on the other hand, ascend via ultraviolet and through the ranges of visible light, of heat, and radar to radio waves. The longest of these are measured in thousands of metres. Figure 2 shows what a very small part of the electromagnetic spectrum gives rise to the sensation of light, when it interacts with the photo-sensitive structures in an animal eye. As we shall see later, some animals 'see' ultraviolet rays for which man is blind, and others have sense organs capable of analysing the distribution of infra-red radiant heat.

Electromagnetic energy and the origin of life

It is pretty certain that short-wave electromagnetic radiation played an important part in the gradual emergence of the living state of matter. The synthesis of large molecules of the nucleic acid and protein type is assumed to have taken place 2,000 to 3,000 million years ago in the primeval oceans or even in the atmosphere under the influence of cosmic radiation and radiation derived from radioactive processes in the earth's crust. The lack of a protective ozone layer in the upper atmosphere at that time gave access to the powerful ultraviolet radiation from the sun. It has been shown experimentally that this part of the electromagnetic spectrum can act as a potent energy source in the chemical synthesis of biomolecules or their forerunners. It is very tempting to go on speculating about the genesis of life on earth and about the part played in it by short-wave electromagnetic radiation.

However, let us go on to safer ground and look at what is happening now. Fortunately for our survival, the intensity of radiation reaching the surface of our planet has for a number of reasons dwindled to a level compatible with the safe existence of complex organisms alive at present. Synthesis of 'living' matter may have ceased altogether. Nevertheless, a certain amount of this radiation still comes through, and there is now added to it a not altogether negligible proportion which is man-made. These sources of electromagnetic energy are probably insufficient to help in creating new life. Yet they can, and do, bring about changes in the hereditary constitution of plants and animals by altering the molecular structure of the genes in the nuclei of reproductive cells. The evolution of the great variety of living organisms during the last 1,000 million years of the earth's history has been helped along by such radiation-induced changes.

Electromagnetic energy as sustainer of life

Let us now put this 'creative' role of radiation on one side, and look at the part it plays in sustaining present life. Here we move along into the 'visible light' part of the spectrum, to the part displayed in our diagram on an expanded scale. It ranges from 390 to 700 mμ. All green plants build up their body substance from simple raw materials such as carbon dioxide, water, and salt by a process known as photo-synthesis, for which sunlight of certain wavelengths is the source of energy. The energy is captured chiefly in the leaves of plants by absorption of light quanta or photons in the molecules of pigments such as green chlorophylls. They are compounds of protein and carotenes. Such pigments may be described as being 'tuned' to certain specific wavelengths. When they are exposed to sunlight they filter out these wavelengths and utilize the energy of the light quanta directly, or hand it on to other substances which may be involved for instance in the synthesis of starch from carbon dioxide and water. Carbohydrates and fats – and, after the take-up of simple nitrogen compounds from the soil, the various proteins – are in this manner incorporated in the body of the growing plant. Plants in turn serve as food for animals. Thus the whole host of living organisms on earth ultimately derive their maintenance energy from cosmic electromagnetic sources, directly or indirectly from the radiation of our parent star, the sun.

Electromagnetic energy and orientation

Once the vital importance of quantum-catching pigments had become established in the course of organic evolution it was only a small step to their utilization in life processes other than body-building photo-synthesis. Receptor organs for electromagnetic radiation became equipped with them to enable them to become tuned to a limited range of wavelengths of sunlight, for their selective absorption. The energy captured in this way by photo-pigments could then be converted into electric signals, which could furnish information for the organism's orientation towards a source of light or within an illuminated field.

Organs equipped in this way with photosensitive pigments

and with nervous structures for the 'transduction' of photo-chemical energy into electric nerve impulses are *light receptors* or *visual organs*. Visual organs need not necessarily be eyes in the accepted sense of the word. They can be of simple design.

It is interesting, though, that, even in the microscopically small unicellular organisms, light-sensitive structures are found which already have most of the essential ingredients of

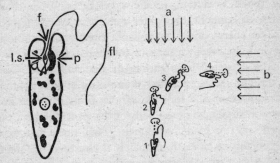

Figure 3. This shows the protozoan Euglena. At the front end there is a funnel (f) from which the whip-like motile flagellum (fl) emerges. The root of the flagellum has a light-sensitive swelling (l.s.) which lies opposite a mass of screening pigment (p). It is shown how the organism orientates to directed light and how it turns when the direction of the light changes from a to b. The manoeuvre is described in the text.

eyes. Figure 3 shows such a light receptor in a flagellate pro-tozoon. The movement of its so-called flagellum is controlled by its base, and this control appears to be related to the amount of light falling on the flagellar root. We find a screen of opaque dark-red or brown pigment on one side of the flagellar root. This allows the organism to orientate its move-ment either towards or away from a source of light. During locomotion the organism rotates around its long axis. While it is aligned in the direction of a light beam, the light-sensitive flagellar root remains exposed to the light throughout rotation.

If, however, the organism deviates from its path towards or away from the light, or when the direction of the light changes, the pigment screen throws a shadow on the light-sensitive root during part of the rotation. This leads to a compensatory turn into the light beam and to reorientation towards the new light direction.

Light is propagated along a straight path, and we have here one of the first examples of an organism reacting to directed light. It may be seen that such direction finding is one of the fundamental aspects of visual orientation. Collecting lenses and pigment screens are found in most visual organs, primitive or sophisticated. It should be noted that screening pigments and photosensitive pigments serve two completely different functions, although they may both be chemically related to carotene.

The design of eyes

Before we deal with the design and function of our own eye, let us look at some of the visual organs found in lower animals. In multicellular animals specialized cells are set aside for light reception. In order to be able to catch light energy they must contain suitable pigments for the selective filtering out of ranges of wavelengths, and they must be equipped to transduce light energy into electric energy either directly or via chemical energy. Finally, they must be able to hand on electric signals to the nervous system of the animal. Visual receptor cells are therefore commonly found to be modified nerve cells in which part of the cell body is set aside to harbour a pigment. A nerve process continuous with the cell body leads off at one end to join similar processes from other similar cells to form a visual nerve. The visual cells of a light receptor or eye are optically insulated from one another by screening pigment. A collecting lens made of highly transparent cells is usually

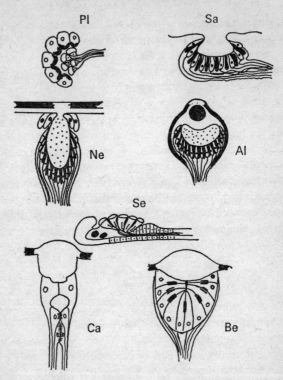

Figure 4. This shows a number of types of primitive eyes in back-boneless animals. They may be considered as the prototypes for the two chief kinds of eye, the lens eye and the compound eye. The eye of the planarian worm (Pl) is a simple cup of pigment cells. Inside the cup are found the cell-bodies of the light-sensitive cells. Such an eye, because of its unilateral screening, is capable of conveying information about the direction of a light beam. The eye of the jelly-fish Sarsia (Sa) is a primitive pit-eye without a lens, and so is the eye of the marine worm Nereis (Ne). The eye of the more active hunting worm Alciopa (Al) has a well-developed lens and vitreous body. The lens serves as a light collector rather than a focusing device. The tube-dwelling sessile worm Serpula (Se) has clusters of light-sensitive cells near the tip of its tentacles. These have a cornea each and can be con-

associated with such a group of visual cells. Two fundamentally different types of eyes can be distinguished right through the evolution from simple to complex eyes. In the one type, the lens eye, an assembly of visual cells forms a so-called retina on to which a simple large lens projects a concentrated beam of light. In the other type, the compound eye, the visual cells are arranged in small groups of up to eight. Each group is provided with a separate refractive lens and screening cells. Thus a compound eye may contain hundreds of 'lenses', each of which concentrates a light beam on to a small number of visual cells. We shall see later how these two types of eye serve two rather different visual functions. Both types range from primitive beginnings to states of high complexity. The most elaborate lens eyes are found in the octopus and cuttle fish among the backboneless animals, and in the vertebrates; whereas the compound eye reaches its highest perfection in the insects. Figure 4 shows a range of eyes of both types on an ascending evolutionary scale of sophistication.

---

sidered to represent primitive ommatidia of the kind that make up the more complex compound eyes of arthropods. Two types of larval eye, one from a caterpillar (Ca) and the other from a beetle larva (Be), show ommatidia which still share a refractive cornea, whereas in the compound eyes of adult insects each ommatidium is provided with its own optical apparatus. The final stages in this double evolutionary series are the human eye (Figure 5) – and the hardly inferior lens eye of a squid or cuttle fish – on the one hand, and the compound eye of an adult insect on the other (Figure 11).

2

THE HUMAN EYE

It is an interesting reflection on how we think in physical rather than in biological terms that one often finds it profitable to explain form and function of the eye by comparing it with a camera rather than proceeding the other way round. This has

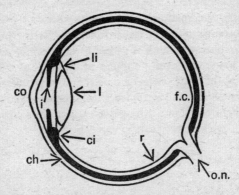

Figure 5. This is a section through the human eye showing the cornea (co), the iris (i), the lens (l) suspended in the ligaments (li) from the ciliary bodies (ci). These are continuous with the iris in front and with the choroid (ch) which contains networks of blood capillaries and dark screening pigment. The retina (r) is seen to be continuous with the optic nerve (o.n.). The point of entry of the optic nerve is the blind spot and the focal area, the fovea centralis (f.c.), surrounded by the yellow macula is indicated by a depression in the retina directly opposite the lens. This part of the retina of our eye consists of cones only.

its historical reason. The physicists were first on the battle-field of science, when biological objects were still shrouded in veils of superstition, taboo, and mystery. Most of our great technological inventions were in fact made without explicit reference to similar biological mechanisms. It is only very recently that 'Bionics' has been instituted as a special branch of technology. In bionics the inquiry into specific technological problems deliberately starts with the question: how does the living organism perform a certain task and what can we learn from it with regard to this or that problem of instrument design? However, physical systems, once in existence, are so infinitely less complex and more 'transparent' than their biological 'prototypes' that it appears to me perfectly permissible to use them as models in the teaching of biology, as long as it is understood that the biological system was functioning smoothly millions of years before the first human artisan got busy.

Here, then, to introduce the fundamentals of form and function of the eye, follows an account of a conversation between student and tutor on the basic design and function of the eye (Figure 5).

We eavesdrop on a tutorial

TUTOR: Have you ever dissected an eye?

STUDENT: Yes, sir, we got some eyes from the slaughter-house and cut them into two halves. It wasn't easy, though, to see all the parts described in the textbook.

TUTOR: I am sure you could describe the various components of a human eye and tell me how they function. But just now I want you to tell me to what piece of apparatus or gadget the eye can be likened.

STUDENT: A camera, sir.

TUTOR: Yes, go ahead.

STUDENT: Both have a lens for focusing an image on a sensitive surface at the back.

TUTOR: Would you describe the focusing mechanism in both cases?

STUDENT: In the camera the lens is moved forwards and backwards with a screw device, but in our eye we change the
shape of the elastic lens.

TUTOR: How?

STUDENT: The lens is suspended between ligaments which
flatten it when the eye is at rest. There are in the ciliary body
a set of muscles which we make contract when we want to
look at a nearby object. When these muscles contract, the
lens becomes less flattened, more spherical.

TUTOR: Do all vertebrate animals focus in this way?

STUDENT: No, I think fish actually move their lenses forwards
like camera lenses.

TUTOR: Yes, this is what all textbooks say, and it may be
correct. However, someone has recently claimed to have
evidence for a different focusing mechanism involving a
change in the shape of the eyeball. This mechanism could
be likened to an extension of the camera bellows.

Talking about the eyeball, it must be borne in mind that,
as in a bellowless modern camera, a lot of precision is
required so far as its dimensions, especially the distance
between cornea and retina, are concerned. Unfortunately,
the critical dimensions of our eyes do not always develop
correctly. In a new-born baby the eyeball is usually too small
or shallow for the lens system, which reaches its final size
sooner. Hence, new-borns are long-sighted. When the eyeball grows, the extent of its growth is in some unknown way
geared to performance. Thus in a schoolchild having a lot of
close-range work to do, the eyeball tends to grow too deep
and the child becomes increasingly short-sighted, especially
if it works and lives under adverse indoor conditions. Can
you tell me how these defects can be corrected?

STUDENT: By the wearing of spectacles, sir.

TUTOR: Obviously, but I want you to give me at least a few
details about this in optical terms.

STUDENT: Well, a short-sighted eye is too long or, better to say, too deep. So, the image of a distant object is formed in front of the retina. You therefore use something that makes the rays converge *less strongly*. This can be achieved by the use of a concave lens. Now the long-sighted eye needs an optical lens which makes the light rays converge *more strongly*, and for that we use a convex lens [Figure 6].

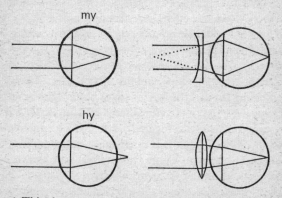

Figure 6. This shows a myopic (my) and a hypermetropic (hy) eye, without and with the appropriate corrective concave and convex spectacle lenses respectively. Explanation in the text.

TUTOR: Do you know the technical terms for short-sightedness and long-sightedness?

STUDENT: I know a short-sighted person is myopic or afflicted with myopia, but I cannot remember the name for long-sightedness.

TUTOR: Hypermetropia. Of course, there are a number of other congenital or acquired eye defects. The most common is the long-sightedness which turns up in middle age.

STUDENT: This is when we need reading glasses? They would be convex, wouldn't they?

TUTOR: Yes. This type of hypermetropia is usually due to a

change in the elasticity of our lens which makes focusing on near objects rather sluggish or impossible. I should like you to keep in mind that myopia and hypermetropia can, of course, be inborn and can be due to a faulty refractive system in a normal-sized eye. Yet another common eye defect is astigmatism which again may be inborn or acquired. It can also be corrected by suitable glasses.

Now let us pursue our analogy between camera and eye farther. When one opens a camera one finds a black coating all over its inside. Has the eye such a coating, and if so what is its function?

STUDENT: Yes, the whole inside of the eyeball is covered by the light-sensitive retina, and this is backed by a layer of cells containing the dark-brown or almost black pigment melanin. This velvety layer of cells absorbs all stray light and thus ensures freedom from fogging or halation, as a photographer would call it. I think it is really more comparable with the coloured backing on highly sensitive plates or film than with the inner coating of the camera body.

TUTOR: This absorption of stray light is certainly a most efficient way of obtaining a clear and well-formed image on the retina. However, animals that are active between dusk and dawn cannot afford to waste any of the incoming light, and we find their eyes equipped with reflecting structures which throw most of the stray light back upon the light-sensitive cells. Of course, both focus and definition suffer in this case, but the smallest differences in illumination can be registered. This is necessary if the vague outlines of friend or foe are to be seen in the gloaming. The presence of such reflectors behind the retina produces the striking eye-shine of nocturnal animals which we see when their eyes are brightly illuminated; for instance, by the headlights of a car.

Let us go back now to the lens. A good camera lens is a

compound structure made of a number of very accurately ground components fitted together tightly. Is the lens of our eye also a complex structure?

STUDENT: Yes, it consists of concentric layers of different refractive power.

TUTOR: That is so, but you must not overlook the fact that, as in all land-living animals, the refraction of the light rays in our eye is shared by the cornea, the transparent and curved wall of the eyeball, by the fluid between cornea and lens known as aqueous humour, by the crystalline lens itself, and by the fluid filling the remainder of the eyeball. In fact, most of the refraction is done by the cornea. The lens serves as a fine-adjustment. Under water, the cornea cannot, of course, function as an important refractive structure, because it has about the same refractive power as water. The lens is, as you say, composed of concentric layers of highly transparent cells whose refractivity increases, as we go from the periphery to the centre. So you see the optical system of the eye is far from simple. We don't want to get involved in geometrical optics, but there is one point I want to make sure you understand. Sharpness of focus does not depend on the refractive structures alone. There is another means of sharpening the focus, and this again has its counterpart in a camera. Can you guess what I am talking of?

STUDENT: I guess you are talking of the iris diaphragm.

TUTOR: Correct.

STUDENT: I believe the chief function of the iris is to control the amount of light to be admitted into the camera or into the eye. The aperture of the iris diaphragm can be increased or decreased in a camera by a complex concentric movement of curved metal lamellae which leave a larger or smaller central hole for the light. In the eye, the choroid, the middle layer of the wall of the eyeball which carries innumerable blood capillaries, is perforated in front by an opening of adjustable diameter, the pupil. The pupil of our own eye is round, but it can have various shapes in other animals. The pupil is surrounded by a complex system of fibres including two sheets of smooth muscles. Their arrangement is circular outside and radial inside. Contraction of the circular muscles closes and that of the radial muscles opens the pupil. The diameter of the pupil is maximal in the dark and on sudden illumination it may become reduced in man to less than half its aperture.

TUTOR: Of course, these dimensions vary in various animals. Think of the cat or the owl, where the speed and degree of closure are very spectacular. Would you know what causes the pupillary reactions?

STUDENT: It is a reflex chiefly brought about by the light falling on the retina.

TUTOR: Does the iris aperture have an influence on the sharpness of the image?

STUDENT: Yes. When one wants maximum sharpness one stops down the diaphragm of the camera to a maximum compatible with the available light. This increases the depth of focus. Similarly in the eye the focal depth is good when distant objects are viewed. As soon as the eye is directed on to a near object the pupil contracts to give optimal visual acuity.

TUTOR: The eyelids are chiefly protective, but in a way they act as a shutter for complete exclusion of light during sleep and on exposure to blinding flashes of light. Strictly speaking, however, there is nothing in our eye to correspond with a camera shutter proper.

STUDENT: Would I be right in saying that the eyelids are chiefly used as windscreen-wipers?

TUTOR: Yes, of course, they help in keeping the cornea moist and in wiping off unwanted particles of dust, etc. The fluid used for this comes from tear glands. Eyelids vary in shape and number in different animals. In some the large movable lid moves downwards, as in ourselves. In others, for instance in some sharks, it moves upwards, and this is always to us an astonishing and unexpected sight. Quite a number of animals, and among them some sharks, have a third transparent eyelid. This so-called nictitating membrane, of which we have only a tiny immobile remnant in the inner corners of our eyes, is the chief windscreen-wiper, for instance in birds and cats. In some aquatic animals it has an additional optical function, in so far as it is transparent and can add to the refractive power of the cornea and lens.

STUDENT: You just mentioned tear glands, sir. What about animals living in water? Do they need to lubricate and rinse the surface of their eyes? In fact, have they got tear glands at all?

TUTOR: One should think that at least marine vertebrates ought to be able to do without them and, in fact, fish have not got any. However, we find glands associated with the eye in turtles. They are modified tear glands and serve the purpose of getting rid of surplus salt from the body. The kidney does not seem to be able to cope sufficiently with salt excretion. When turtles go on land to lay eggs they can be observed to 'cry' copiously. Sea-snakes, too, have similar glands. The brakish water terrapin can produce tears with a high salt content.

Sea-birds like the cormorant, the mallard duck, and the penguin have nasal glands that serve the same purpose. You may wonder why I haven't mentioned the proverbial crocodiles' tears. This is because scientific information on them, even in the freshwater crocodiles whose tears are proverbial, is surprisingly scarce.

STUDENT: Maybe nobody wants to go near enough to a crocodile to sample its tears!

TUTOR: By the way, the shedding of tears from emotion

seems to be confined to man. Even our closest relatives, the apes and monkeys, do not shed tears in anger or distress. Before you go, I want to make sure you know how the eyes are moved about in their sockets when we scan the world around us.

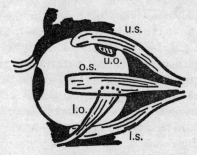

Figure 7. This shows five of the six eye muscles. The eye is seen from the direction of the temple (outside). The outer, upper, and lower straight (o.s., u.s., l.s.) muscles are visible along their whole course, and so is the lower oblique (l.o.) muscle, except for its insertion on the eyeball. This lies under the outer straight muscle. The insertion of the upper oblique muscle (u.o.) can be seen projecting from under the upper straight muscle. The inner straight muscle on the nasal side of the eyeball (inside) is completely hidden. It can easily be imagined what eye movements result from the contraction of individual muscles, if it is remembered that they work antagonistically in pairs. When one member of a pair contracts, the other relaxes simultaneously. (*Modified after Duke-Elder.*)

STUDENT: We have three pairs of muscles attached to the eye-ball. One pair, the horizontal straight eye muscles, move the eye to and fro between nose and temples; another pair, the upper and lower straight eye muscles, lift or lower our gaze; and the third pair, which are inserted obliquely on the upper and lower surface of the eyeball, can make the eye roll about the axis connecting the centre of the cornea with the centre of the retina [Figure 7].

TUTOR: This is correct. Of course, you realize that all these eye movements can also be executed involuntarily, in order to keep our gaze on target while our head changes its position in space either actively or passively. You will hear about this when we discuss the maintenance of balance and posture [Chapter 6].

The retina

We have been eavesdropping on a tutorial, and it may be conceded that the student was rather well informed and interested in his subject. We are now going to have a close look at the real business-end of the eye, the light-sensitive retina. The electron-microscope has of recent years given us a completely new idea of the intimate structure of the retinal cells and it will be interesting to see how this has helped us in unravelling the complicated process involved in vision. But before we go into all this it may be useful to consider the more obvious and crude aspects of vision. We know that the optical system of the eye projects an image of whatever we look at on to the retina. This image is very much reduced in size and, for optical reasons, upside down. It consists of areas of different brightness and, of course, also of different colour. Somehow this image must be transduced into a pattern of electric pulses. These are conducted to the brain, where they reach the highest optical centres that lie at the back of our head. A proper functioning of all this is necessary for us to 'see' what we are looking at, but it cannot be emphasized too strongly that it is quite impossible to know how the electric events going on in the nervous system give rise to our conscious visual experience. We shall have more to say about this in the last chapter.

The retina is usually compared with the photographic plate in a camera. It is true, both are highly light sensitive and both are composed of a very great number of discrete light-sensitive units, particles of silver salt in the emulsion of the plate, and the minute rods and cones which make up the inner layer of the retina of the eye. In both, therefore, the image is cut up into a grid of separate points, each of which receives a portion of the light energy – a lot in the bright and less in the darker areas of the image. In each of these points illumination produces a change, and it is here that the analogy between photographic plate and retina begins to break down. In the grains of the photographic plate the light produces a lasting photochemical change. This can be made evident by consequent development in which the silver salt which has absorbed the light energy becomes irreversibly reduced to the metallic silver of the negative: the more light, the denser the layer of silver grains on the negative. In contrast to this the changes in the retinal cells – although also photochemical – are completely reversible, and the imprint of the image on the retina is extremely short-lived. At each of the grid points the photochemical effect of illumination is instantly transduced into electrical pulses, whose frequency depends on the intensity of the light, and the photochemical receptiveness is equally rapidly restored. In a way the eye resembles a television camera in which the brightness distribution of an optical image is analysed and transduced into patterns of electrical pulses.

The ultrastructure of the retina

The retina consists of about 130 million rods and cones. These are modified nerve cells, and they are connected by nerve fibres to larger nerve cells immediately beneath the retina – and these in turn are connected to the brain via the optic nerve. A rod or cone consists of a cell body, which is divided into two segments (Figure 8). The lower of the two segments is the cell body proper, equipped as usual with a nucleus and with all those cell inclusions that belong to a cell in full working order. It may be said that the cell inclusions that are necessary for the maintenance of a high level of energy

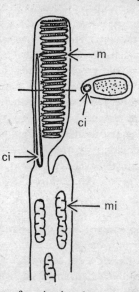

Figure 8. This is part of a visual rod as seen under the electron-microscope. The end segment contains a stack of membranes (m) carrying the molecules of photosensitive pigment. The cilium-like part of the end segment (ci) can be seen in cross-section. It has nine peripheral filaments but lacks the two central ones of a true cilium. The penultimate segment of the rod contains mitochondria (mi), which are an important item in the chemical machinery of the living cell. The nucleus is not shown. It lies still farther away from the end segment. The 11,000 membranes of the end segment are here diagrammatically represented by only a few. The picture is based on a reconstruction from many thousands of ultra-thin sections.

turn-over, known as mitochondria, are present in profusion. At its base the inner segment gives rise to a nerve process which makes connexion with a process of junctional nerve cells in the central layer of the retina. These make connexion with the ganglion cells whose long processes form the optic nerve. Under the electron-microscope, we can resolve the ultrastructure of the upper of these two segments, and the astonishing fact emerges that this end segment is a modified cilium, or hair process. The cilia, in simple, unicellular organisms, have a definite function: they move the organism about. They are motile processes which beat the water like miniature oars. In the body cavities of higher animals, sheets of ciliated cells propel fluids along by their concerted action. For instance, there are such cilia in our windpipe. They are responsible for the rejection of foreign particles and slime which are wafted along by them. It is surprising to find modified cilia within the eyeball.

Rods and cones as quantum catchers

The cilium in the end segment of the retinal rod, although it is not motile at all, has a structure resembling that of a normal cilium by having a set of nine longitudinal filaments. On one side this cilium widens into a bag which forms the bulk of the end segment. This is filled with a system of transverse double membranes – like a column of pennies one above the other. There are about 11,000 of them in each rod. These membranes carry an orderly assembly of millions of molecules of visual pigment. And so a ray of light which strikes the end segment of a rod or cone is aimed at roughly 2,000 million pigment molecules. Any one of these can catch a light quantum, the minutest quantity of light energy. In doing so, it undergoes a subtle change in its chemical structure. Such a photochemical process is the first step in light perception, and is itself a most intriguingly complex affair. Let us have a look at it in more detail.

The photosensitive pigments that are used in visual organs

are compounds of retinene, which is a derivative of vitamin A, and of a protein called an opsin. Together they form, for instance, the pigment rhodopsin or visual purple. Substances like this are called conjugated proteins, and they play an important part in all types of life processes: haemoglobin and chlorophyll are other examples. In the visual system, the role of visual pigment is to catch light quanta or photons. Imagine now a giant opsin molecule, with its irregular outer surface. Embedded in its surface – just fitting into a specially shaped space – nestles the retinene molecule. Retinene molecules come in a number of different shapes, according to the run of their molecular chain. Some are stable, others have kinks in their chain and are unstable: these can straighten out again under impact. Retinene 11 cis, which fits into the opsin molecule, has such a kink. But when it is hit by a photon it straightens into retinene all-trans, and the straight all-trans retinene now no longer fits into the space on the opsin surface. In fact, one imagines it jumping out like an uncoiling spring, under the influence of the energy of a light quantum.

The excitatory process

Two things may happen now, and we are not sure which. The newly exposed surface of the opsin molecule may act like a catalyst – an enzyme – and set in motion a chain of chemical reactions. It is quite plausible that this process may result in the build-up within the rod of an electric potential, and that this is ultimately responsible for making an adjacent nerve cell fire a series of coded impulses. Alternatively, an electric potential may be directly generated across the membrane in which the opsin molecule sits. It has been suggested that by liberating the retinene from the opsin the photon may, so to speak, punch a mono-molecular hole into the excitable membrane, and so upset its electrical balance. But either possibility leaves a mysterious gap. They both give us some idea of how a retinal rod may produce an electric potential proportional to the amount of light hitting it – but where exactly is this potential transformed into a series of coded impulses? And what has

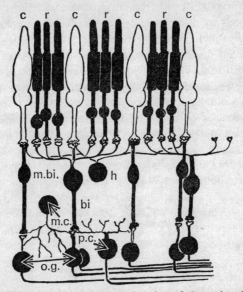

Figure 9. This is a schematic representation of the retina. Rods (r) and cones (c) are shown intermingled and it can be seen that cones make synaptic contact with so-called midget-bipolar (m.bi.) ganglion cells which – in turn – synapse with the ganglion cells whose axons form the optic 'nerve'. Here a one-to-one connexion is symbolized. In contrast to this a number of rods are joined to single optic ganglion cells by the processes of larger bipolar cells (bi). Cross-connexions do, however, exist between cones. They are furnished by the horizontal cells (h). The so-called parasol ganglion cells (p.c.) interconnect the two types of bipolar cells, and the rods and cones and optic ganglion cells (o.g.) can be seen to be interconnected by 'monopolar' ganglion cells (amacrine cells) without a central axon (m.c.). The pigment layer into which the tips of the rods and cones dip is omitted for the sake of simplicity.

the ciliary structure to do with all this? Frankly, we don't know.

In our eye, as in the eye of all vertebrate animals, the light-sensitive cells form the outermost layer of the retina. Their tips or terminal segments dip into a layer of cells containing dark pigment. They belong to the choroid coat of the eyeball. Rods and cones can differ considerably in shape, but much more important is the way their nerve processes make connexion with the junctional neurons, which connect them with the ganglion cells in the inner layer of the retina. As can be seen from Figure 9, a number of neighbouring rods jointly make connexion with junctional neurons with many nerve processes. Cones, however, can be connected singly to cells of the ganglion cell layer by bipolar junctional neurons. There are other junctional cells in the various layers of the retina, and these appear to be able to make a variety of cross-connexions between neighbouring groups of rods and cones. One day this bewildering network of connexions will find its proper functional explanation. However, we shall have occasion later to refer to some of the possible reasons for this complex arrangement. One thing is clear, the image on the retina is certainly never subdivided into 130 million independent grid points, and it would be wrong therefore to assess the resolving power of our eye on the basis of this figure.

3

VISION

The visual image

VISUAL orientation involves the recognition of objects and of their position relative to one another and to the observer. It involves the accurate judging of distance and, of course, the tracking of moving objects and the prediction of direction and speed of their movement. We have seen how the environment is projected on to the retina of the eye in the form of a tiny upside-down image. This image is transmitted to the brain by means of an orderly pattern of electric impulses. The final result is our conscious awareness of three-dimensional space, filled with objects. They have solidity, size, colour, and location. When we deal with the tactile sense it will be seen that we are capable of accurately pinpointing the exact spot on our fingertip which receives a tactile stimulus. We do not in a similar way consciously locate the little image of the world on our retina as lying at the back of our eye. On the contrary, we project the image outwards, and so the big world assumes its proper scale. How do we know how big it is, if all we have to go on with is the tiny image on our retina? Visual information alone cannot account for this. We judge this from experience gained by handling things and by moving around among them. It is experience that helps us to 'externalize' the visual stimulus.

In fact, we hardly ever localize visual sensations within the eyeball. When we close our eyes after having looked at a very bright object, we see an 'after-image' of the object floating somewhere in space at a rather undefined distance. Gentle pressure on the eyeball, or of course much more so a blow on the eye, produce the appearance of coloured patterns in our visual field. These, too, are rather vaguely localized, and so are the dark spots before the eyes or '*mouches volantes*' which are the shadow images of impurities floating in the eye fluid or, under certain conditions of illumination, the image of the blood capillaries in the retina itself. Such phenomena are very interesting, and the study of some of them has been useful for the understanding of the visual process, especially of colour vision. But they have little part to play in the daily business of living and can be left on one side, while we explore the mysteries of seeing the world.

Three-dimensional vision

We stand in front of a painting of a French street scene by Utrillo. What fascinates us, apart from the whiteness of the blue-shuttered houses, is the sensation of depth, the street leading away from the foreground inviting us to walk along and peep round a far-away street corner to see where we could go from there. And yet this is a flat canvas with a fraction of an inch of oil paint on it, and it is to all intents and purposes two-dimensional. Our appreciation of space in this picture can teach us a lot about 'real' visual space. Our retina, too, is practically two-dimensional. Let us see what clues we use when we project the image on it outwards, and literally make of it the world we live in. It is well known that stereoscopic vision, or vision in depth, is attributed to the fact that the images from our paired eyes are not identical and that their overlap produces the sensation of three-dimensionality. In gadgets known as stereoscopes two copies of a picture taken from a slightly different angle are mounted side by side at a certain critical distance from one another. They are viewed through two lenses, and one remembers the sensation of relief experienced when, during the adjustment of distance and focus, the two images at last unite to give the 'stereo-picture'.

The picture is now apparently filled with space and air and the objects stand out boldly, each in its proper place, and each 'as if we could walk around it'.

It is true that, on shutting one eye, we can become temporarily unable to judge distances, and catch ourselves trying to get hold of an object beyond the reach of our arm. This is exactly what infants do before they have acquired sufficient tactile experience to learn what is near and far!

After a while, however, we realize that we are quite able to judge distances with only one eye. Knowing the size of objects, say a man's height as compared with that of a boy, we realize that the boy is near and the man quite a distance away, if the image on the retina of the person in children's clothes is twice the apparent height of that representing the adult man. Similarly, we do not jump to the conclusion that a car racing away from us is shrinking. The outlines of objects standing one behind the other are another clue. The object whose outlines are unobscured by those of the other is the nearer one. Depth sensation is also aided by the phenomena of perspective. The apparent narrowing of the road, and the downward slope of the roof-line of a long building alongside it, are symbols of distance, and so is the haziness of a far-away mountain range.

Shading puts bulk into objects. Of course, if we did not know about the significance of shading, we could be made to believe that one side of a lamp-post was painted darker than the other. As it is, we recognize its roundness and thickness by the difference of its sunny and shady aspects. Anyone having travelled in tropical parts knows how flat and uninteresting the landscape looks at noon, when the sun is right overhead, and when there is very little shade to throw objects into relief.

If – still with one eye closed – I want to know for certain which of two trees is the nearer, I move my head from side to side and the relative position of the two trees changes. The image of the more distant tree appears to be displaced behind the almost stationary image of the nearer one. This is known as 'parallax'. Parallax, by the way, plays an important part in the astronomer's measurements of the distances of stars. If two stars are photographed at an interval of six months when we ourselves have moved from one end of our elliptical path round the sun to the other, the image of the more distant star is displaced relative to that of the other, and the amount of displacement is a measure of the distance between the stars. A telescope is one-eyed and yet capable of revealing depth.

Seeing seems to be a rather calculating business, and all this makes one wonder whether one can ever 'see' something of which one has had no previous knowledge. We gain this impression also from patients, blind from childhood, on whom normal vision has been bestowed by an operation. Previous to this 'opening of the eyes', they had been living in a world of tactile experience, of sound and scent, full of objects familiar to them in terms of their restricted range of sensory experience. How they shrink at first from the welter of additional stimulation, longing at times to return to the relative seclusion of their former world! One of the most striking facts is that it takes a lot of time and effort before they recognize the objects around them as separate items. They have gradually to learn to 'make sense of them' by associating their visual appearance with their tactile and other properties familiar to them. 'At first sight' the world looks like a flat extension of meaningless patches of light, dark, and colour jumbled up into a quilt work. One by one objects grow out of this chaotic world, and remain unmistakably separate once they have been identified. A student of microscopy experiences something similar. A meaningless jumble of shapes defies description, until the demonstrator has drawn on paper one or the other specific shapes to be searched for. The saying 'seeing is believing' may fittingly be reversed in this context into 'believing is seeing'.

During our excursion into matters of visual experience, we

might be tempted to make a tour of the rather hackneyed examples of optical illusions found in all schoolbooks, textbooks of classical physics and of physiology, and even in week-end almanacs. If properly analysed, it is true, they can teach us a lot, not only of the way our brain interprets the information received by the retina but also about the functioning of the retina itself. However, on balance, it may be more useful in our comparative study of sense organs to pay attention to some of the more quantitative aspects of visual function.

Visual acuity

Our power to recognize patterns depends on, among other things, our sharpness of vision or visual acuity. This becomes overridingly important when we want to spot a small object at a distance, or when we try to make out the contours of a number of overlapping objects. The question then is: what is the smallest object distinguishable against its background at such and such a distance? To assess this, we return to the image on the retina. It stands to reason that a special feature of this image can be distinguished from the rest only if it is capable of sending a special discrete message about its presence up the optic nerve. It must therefore not be smaller shan a single receptor unit. This is in the best of cases a single cone in the fovea of the retina. We have seen in Chapter 2 that only cones may make separate through connexion with the optic centre, by means of a certain type of bipolar junctional neuron. Rods are always grouped. A number of them make joint contact with junctional neurones. Such a group also acts as a visual unit, but its receptive surface may be several hundred times larger than that of a single cone. Within it elements of the visual image cannot possibly be separately recorded, however much they may differ in brightness or outline from one another.

As we all know, sharpness of vision also depends on illumination. In dim light a good-sized pebble may escape our notice, whereas we see individual specks of dust in bright sunshine. The reason for this is that our cones are rather insensitive; in fact, they don't function at all in dim light. At night the fovea, the area of sharpest vision is therefore practically blind, and we rely entirely on the rods, which, although sensitive to the smallest trace of light, work joined together in groups. The number that are so joined together is not given once and for all by permanent synaptic connexions with junctional neurones, but can be increased or decreased automatically in accordance with the general state of illumination. The darker it is, the larger the groups of rods working in unison. This is just one of the many automatic control mechanisms which we are constantly coming across in biological systems. This means that, under conditions of reduced illumination, sharpness of pattern discrimination is sacrificed in favour of overall sensitivity. The greater the number of hounds, the greater the chance of catching the hare. When there are only few light quanta coming in per unit time, more quantum-catching rods are linked together to pool their excitation. This means a greater chance that an impulse is successfully triggered off to signal the presence of light. Of course, enlargement of the visual unit means a proportional increase in the minimum size of objects that can just be distinguished from others or from their background.

Camera design and the eye

In this connexion it might be instructive to have a look at camera design. Photographers know that our modern cameras with their large lenses of wide aperture and short focal length are wonderful light catchers, permitting astonishingly short exposures. But at full aperture, the sharpness of the picture, even on fine grain film, leaves much to be desired, and so does the depth of focus.

A wide-aperture lens has to be of first-class make to have only a minimum of the optical imperfections to be expected in such a large piece of glass. Spherical and chromatic aberration are terms with a disagreeable sound to the lens maker. They mean that the image is likely to be blurred in outline and to abound with coloured fringes which spoil its sharpness and definition. We may pride ourselves in the possession of a camera with a big lens of a low number, say two or even lower. This number is arrived at by dividing the focal length by the diameter. However, we have frequently to throw away quite a good deal of the superb light-collecting power of the lens by stopping down the diaphragm in order to get better depth of focus and sharpness. All the same, in a large-diameter lens a larger proportion of the lens in the centre is relatively free from the usual imperfections which become more difficult to correct near the margin.

Animal optics

A lens with a long focal length and a smaller diameter, and consequently with a larger number, say 4·5 or even 8, collects much less light, but it projects a relatively sharper image over a larger area of visual units. We find both types of lens in animals of different habitat and mode of life. Let us look at a number of types of eye and see how our optical principles are utilized to serve best under different circumstances (Figure 10). Take the eye of a mouse first. The mouse is a nocturnal animal normally moving about in the dark. It relies, in its orientation, on its sense of touch, hearing, and smell more than on sight. It has, however, many enemies among fellow mammals and birds, and their approach is often literally 'foreshadowed' by a darkening of the scene. A moving shadow or dark mass obscures the field of vision. It is too late to worry whether the foe offers a pretty or an ugly sight, or whether it is beast or fowl, and good pattern discrimination would be of little use. The mouse eye is admirably adapted for its task. A lens, enormous in proportion to a tiny eyeball – filling it almost completely – lies close to the retina. Such a lens, with its wide aperture, collects every available scrap of light – never mind

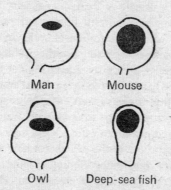

Man   Mouse

Owl   Deep-sea fish

Figure 10. This shows the relative proportion of lens to eye in the eye of man, mouse, owl, and deep-sea fish. Their actual sizes are vastly different. They are here reduced to or enlarged to the same size in order to illustrate the differences in proportions.

how badly defined the image. Such proportionally large lenses are also found in deep-sea fish. Light is scarce in the abyssal depths of the ocean. Most of it emanates from living organisms by what is known as bio-luminescence. Animal light is one of the most fascinating chapters of biology. So far as our story of eyes is concerned, it is of absorbing interest that some of the light-emitting structures in deep-sea fish are eyes in reverse, in so far as the light is chemically produced in an organ that has almost all the gadgetry of an eye. There is a light-producing tissue corresponding to the retina and an optical apparatus complete with lens and other refractive structures, and with reflectors, and a shutter. These searchlight organs can flash light at intervals as they can be switched off, if need arises, by the shutter.

But let us return to the eyes of deep-sea fish. They have, in some cases, lenses so large in proportion to the size of the fish that a spherical eye into which they could fit would be much too bulky for the head. It must be remembered that deep-sea fish are usually very tiny – unexpectedly so for someone who has only seen fantastic illustrations of them and their bizarre shapes without indication of scale. In such cases, so-called telescopic eyes seem to solve the problem of bulk. The eye is cylindrical – a very large lens lies opposite a retina of small surface area, and the restricted visual angle is made good by high mobility of the stalked eye. Quite apart from their light-gathering power, large lenses are necessary in all aquatic animals; their cornea is optically useless under water.

In contrast, the eye of the owl shows how a bulging hemi-spherical cornea contributes the lion's share to the refractive power of the eye in a land-living animal. Here the lens is relatively small, but the eye with its roughly tubular shape reminds us of that of a deep-sea fish. Our own eye is a typical all-purpose eye. It is characterized by an optically efficient curved cornea, a relatively small but adjustable lens, and a large-area retina with a central fovea of densely packed partly independently circuited cones. These are surrounded at the periphery by assemblies of rods joined in visual units of hundreds of interconnected quantum catchers. In daylight the fovea yields accurate pattern discrimination and also, as will be seen presently, colour vision. The peripheral parts of the retina are operative in dim light where their sensitivity can be up to a million times greater than that of the fovea. How our light-sensitivity increases in the dark is vividly demonstrated to all amateur photographers using a make-shift dark room. At first entry one is tremendously pleased with one's efforts at blacking out, but alas, after ten minutes the various chinks of light become painfully obvious, and one feels one could read the paper in the blessed place!

More about visual acuity

Visual acuity is measured in terms of the angle subtended at the eye by the smallest object that can just be picked out from its background. In dim light, this amounts to half a degree at the so-called nodal point of the light path in the eye, a point which lies near the inner surface of the lens. This produces an image at the retina covering thousands of rods. In bright daylight much smaller objects subtending only half a minute of arc can be resolved.

This brings us down to the dimensions of single cones, as their diameter of $1.5\,\mu$ corresponds to half a minute of arc at the nodal point. This means that the image of a small object can be distinguished from that of a neighbouring one, if there is at least one unstimulated cone between them. In fact, the two images must be at least $1.5\,\mu$ apart on the fovea of the retina.

During the war I used to wonder how it was that I could follow the steel cable of the captive barrage balloons quite clearly up to great heights against the bright sky. The angle subtended by such a cable surely was smaller than a minute of an arc. My ponderings were in fact quite justified. For a single line on a uniform background or for a slight discontinuity of a line seen on measuring something with a finely graduated vernier scale, say on a sliderule, the resolving power is 0.5 to 4 seconds of arc, according to circumstances. This resolution is up to sixty times higher than for ordinary objects. Why this is so has baffled the experts considerably, and a number of explanations have been proposed. The simplest one is based on the fact that our eyes are never still, and that the image of a long, thin, dark line will, therefore, move to and fro on the retina, slightly darkening now one, now another line of hundreds of cones simultaneously. This simultaneous event in a great number of cones provides information about an object the image of which falls well within the diameter of a single cone.

The incessant small-scale movements of our eyes are, in fact, the only way in which we can see stationary patterns. If head and eyeball are completely immobilized in a human observer, and a complex stationary pattern is shown to him on a screen, he sees it for a very short while only. The pattern then becomes blurred and even disappears. Thus continuous small-scale scanning seems to be necessary for clear vision. Moving objects, of course, are most easily picked out, because their image moves across the retina, stimulating one set of receptors after another. Recent delicate work on the responses from single retinal receptors and their effects on the nerve cells in the visual areas of the brain have shown that there are, in the retina, receptors which respond to the movement of retinal images in one specific direction only. Groups of receptors have been found to be concerned with the analysis of certain specific shapes of image such as a straight edge, or a curved contour, or a sharp-angled one.

It can thus be said that the retina of a certain animal has, during evolution, become so organized as to select a specific range of biologically important stimuli from others of less biological significance. For instance, there are units in the eye of a frog which are especially highly sensitive to the movement of the image of a small dark spot across the retina, such as would be projected by a fly buzzing across the visual field. The nervous connexions between the sensory cells of the retina are quite clearly themselves patterned, and not at all as random as they might appear on microscopic examination of a section through the eye. It appears that, apart from our having to learn individually how to make sense of the bewildering patterns of the world around us, each species of animal may have, during its evolution, acquired the power to pick out the biologically important information from the welter of ever-present ever-changing visual stimuli on which they literally turn a blind eye.

The compound eye

We have seen that our lens eye is not the only possible solution to the design of a complex visual organ. The compound eye of the insects and other arthropods like shrimps, lobsters, and crabs is based on a completely different principle of arrangement and components (Figure 11). It is true that each of the units known as ommatidia contains a set of structures that correspond to what we find in our eye. There is a lens-like refractive body, the outer cover of which is, like our cornea, a transparent part of the general body-wall. The crystalline cone refracts the light so as to project it on to an assembly of visual cells. These so-called retinula cells are elongated structures, and are arranged to stand in a circlet around a central axis. Their number varies in different eyes. Let us say our ommatidium contains seven such retinula cells. Each retinula cell has a striated border. All seven striated borders face each other and together make up the central core of the ommatidium. This is known as the rhabdome. It will be remembered that the end segment of the rods and cones in our eye contains stacks of lamellae which are the seat of the groups of molecules of light-sensitive visual pigment. The electron-microscope reveals that the rhabdome of the compound eye harbours a similar arrangement of membranes. It is therefore in the rhabdome that the photochemical events of the visual process take place. Each retinula cell, like our rods and cones, constitutes a modified neuron and is, therefore, continuous with a nerve process. The seven nerve processes of each ommatidium run in parallel to make synaptic contact with the neurons of the optic nerve mass which, like the various ganglion cells of our retina, lies actually within the eye and represents an outpost of the central nervous system. There are systems of pigment cells which are used to screen the ommatidia from one another. Often these screens are movable so

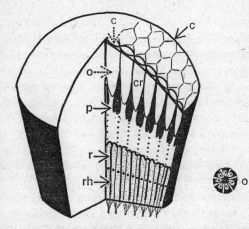

Figure 11. This is a schematic representation of the design of a compound eye. A curved, faceted cornea (c) is made up of the corneal parts of the individual ommatidia (o). Seven ommatidia are shown in longitudinal section. Apart from the cornea they have each a crystalline cone (cr). Pigment cells (p) insulate these cones from one another. The pigment cells can elongate downward so as to form complete curtains of dark pigment between the ommatidia. The light-sensitive part of each ommatidium consists in this case of seven retinula cells (r) standing around a central axis which is made up of the striated borders of these cells. This central structure is called the rhabdome (rh) and is thought to be the seat of the light-sensitive pigment. The light is focused on to the rhabdome. The retinula cells send nerve fibres into a ganglion immediately below the retina. An enlarged cross-section through an ommatidium shows seven cells and their central rhabdome.

that the ommatidia can be presented to the light singly or in groups. Insects that are active in day and night make use of such screens to adapt their eyes to the amount of light available, making use of every photon of it in dim illumination by pooling their ommatidia with screens withdrawn or, in broad daylight, by absorbing superfluous light in the dark pigment of the screening cells enveloping each ommatidium. In this case, each ommatidium is an isolated optical unit and the compound eye an assembly of many separately functioning eyes. Among the insects the number of ommatidia making up a compound eye varies from a few to a few thousands and the absolute size of the eyes varies accordingly. Some beetles have very small eyes, and in a dragonfly the eyes are the most prominent part of the head. What is important is the number of ommatidia per unit surface area of the faceted cornea. This number is an indication of the power of resolution of the eye, just as in the case of the rods and cones in our retina. The angle of vision of single ommatidia varies accordingly between 1° in the honey bee and 20° in a species of woodlouse or slater among the crustaceans.

All this raises a very interesting point. Does every single ommatidium project a complete image of its field of vision on to its seven or so retinula cells, and, if so, is the total image with which the visual centre deals composed of a mosaic of as many separate pictures as there are ommatidia? Does this mean that insects see a patchwork world? In a way this is in fact true. Even the most efficient insect eye consists of only a few thousand ommatidia, which have to cover the whole visual field, whereas our retina contains millions of potentially independent visual units serving a similar field of vision. The resolution of the insect eye and the detail of pattern they can appreciate is therefore bound to be poor. On the other hand, it appears that the insect eye is an excellent detector for movement. The outlines of objects moving across the visual field, or of stationary objects in relative movement during rapid flight, cross and recross the sharp boundaries between the independent ommatidia, switching them on and off in a sequence, depending on the speed and direction of the moving object. Moreover, insects can see discrete events that follow each other at a very high frequency. Whereas, for us, events separated by less than one thirty-fifth of a second become

Figure 12. This illustrates pattern discrimination by insects. All patterns in the upper row can be distinguished from any pattern in the lower row. Insects are, however, usually incapable of distinguishing between the patterns contained within the upper or those within the lower row.

fused, in an 'insect cinema' the projector would have to race along at 350 frames per second to give the 'insect audience' the illusion of smooth continuity in time. This enables insects to appreciate movement to an extent quite unimaginable to us. Bees can be trained to distinguish between patterns, and it has been shown that they most easily recognize a pattern which is rich in contour in relation to overall size. In fact, objects with the same relative amount of contour cannot be distinguished from one another by bees (Figure 12). Bees may therefore recognize flowers in this way rather than by 'image'. The subdivision of each ommatidium into a number of retinula cells seems to be of functional importance in colour vision in the appreciation of the plane of polarization of light (see later and Chapter 4).

Limits of visual sensitivity

Our eyes are most sensitive to blue-green light of a wavelength of 500 mμ. This is so because the visual purple of rhodopsin in our retinal rods absorbs more of this wavelength than of any others, longer or shorter. It is always interesting to find out what is the minimum quantity of a stimulus that can just be perceived by a human observer or reacted to by an animal. One speaks of a threshold stimulus in this connexion. The term is self-explanatory. It must be obvious by now that the visual threshold values for our eye must vary with the circumstances: above all, with the background illumination.

Let us, then, assume that we have dark-adapted our eyes by staying in a good dark room for about half an hour. A short flash of light of 500 mμ wavelength and of a beam-width of 10 seconds of arc at the nodal point is offered to our eye, so that the image falls on a few hundred rods somewhere in the periphery of the retina. Under these conditions it takes a light intensity delivering between 1 and 10 quanta per rod to make us aware of the flash. The total energy conveyed in such a flash is incredibly minute. As Dr Pirenne of Oxford has recently pointed out, the mechanical energy needed to lift a single pea 1 inch above the table – if totally converted into electromagnetic quanta – would be sufficient to produce such a just visible flash in the eyes of all human beings that have ever walked the earth.

A relatively larger test image of about 1·5 cm.^{2} on the retina can just be seen against a dark background, when only one of every 6,000 rods receives 1 quantum of light per second.

This explains why we can see outlines and shapes when walking about in the dark when most of our retinal receptors are unstimulated. In bright moonlight the sky emits over 20,000 times more light than is necessary for threshold stimulation. Each single rod now receives 3 or even 4 quanta per second. Pattern vision is therefore pretty good, and we can read the paper without much difficulty.

Colour vision

We have been talking of wavelengths of light, and in one instance we described light of 500 mμ as blue-green. All normal human subjects would describe it as such, and they would be able to ascribe a series of hues or colours to the various regions of a spectrum projected on a screen by means of a glass prism. This refracts white light in such a way that the various wavelengths which make up white light come to lie in different places on the screen. The colours of such a spectrum range from blue on the left via blue-green and yellow-green, green-orange to red on the extreme right in a conventional projection. Totally colour-blind people also see the spread-out light beam and distinguish in it quite a number of regions that appear to them differently luminous – but they have no sensation of colour. Not all colour-defective people are totally colour-blind. They may see altogether fewer hues in a coloured spectrum that may be shortened at one or the other end. Their condition may be an inherited one and is generally more common in men than in women. 'Monochromat' subjects are totally incapable of distinguishing any colour from any other of equal luminance. They are found equally among both sexes. 'Dichromate' subjects see colour, but have difficulty in distinguishing certain colours. Protanope and deuteranope dichromates fail to distinguish blue-green from white and red; yellow and orange look alike to them. The protanopes cannot see red at all. Two per cent of males in this country are protanope or deuteranope dichromates.

Tritanope dichromates have good colour discrimination at the red end of the spectrum, but have great difficulty in distinguishing blue from green.

In 6 per cent of the male population we find minor abnormalities in colour matching by which they differ from the rest of the population. They are known as 'anomalous trichromates'. All these forms of defective colour vision, apart from their obvious implications in professional selection for jobs requiring normal colour discrimination, have been of great scientific interest. They can help us to understand the mechanism of normal colour vision. We may have to say more about them later. Meanwhile, it almost looks as if we took colour vision and the enjoyment of a colourful world for granted. Yet only a relatively few of our fellow animals appear to have colour vision and there are many differences between them with regard to the number and kinds of hues they can see and discriminate.

The advantages of colour vision

Colour vision obviously adds enormously to the richness of visual experience in us, and to the amount of visual information available to animals in general. It is therefore of great value to all animals that are chiefly active in day-time. In darkness and in dim light colours are unimportant in nature. Of course, it is a different matter in Piccadilly Circus, Times Square, or Pigalle. Here, as quite generally in our modern world, colour has invaded the night both for the sake of conveying information and for the sheer joy of it. In a way the coloured lights of the bio-luminescent creatures of the deep sea are of comparable significance.

A 'coloured object' is one the surface of which either reflects or emits electromagnetic waves over a limited range of wave-lengths. As we shall see in Chapter 11, this is all there is to it. Colour sensation and reaction to colour arise in the organism when radiation affects the visual organs and the nerve centres connected with them.

How, then, can we make so bold as to state that such and such an animal sees colour or is colour-blind? In fact, all we can find out with a certain degree of confidence is whether they react differently to objects of different colour, and not just distinguish bright from dark. We can only surmise that an animal that can do this 'experiences' something akin to our own sensation of colour, and here we tread on very dangerous ground indeed. Let us follow through one or the other of the experiments that have convinced biologists of the presence of colour vision in animals, and let us for this purpose investigate an insect, a fish, and a fellow mammal.

How to demonstrate colour vision in animals

In choosing our insect it may be as well to select one of which we know that it visits the blossoms of flowering plants. Their beautiful colours might well serve as signs for recognition, enabling the insect to return to a flower that offers pollen or nectar in profusion rather than having to try all the various plants in a meadow one after another, repeatedly taking 'pot-luck'. As we shall see later, the scent of flowers can serve as such a sign-post, but the more information, the less effort wasted. We have a dual task. We must show first that the insect reacts to a specific colour, and second, that it distinguishes it from other colours and – more important still – from shades of grey of similar luminosity. Let us assume that field observation has disclosed that a certain hover fly has been visiting almost exclusively a certain blue flower on its foraging flights across a meadow. We now push some decoy flowers of blue paper in among the real blossoms and watch. Our decoys should be flower-like, but it may be as well that we don't give them the same shape as their natural counterparts. Otherwise we might be led to assume our insects were attracted by the similarity of shape, if we found them to pay repeated unrewarding visits to the decoys. In fact, that is what they do. Again and again they alight on the decoy flowers, despite their difference in shape and despite the total absence of scent. We also have put some yellow and red decoys among the others. They are ignored. So, it looks as if 'blueness' was recognized and selected by the insect. A glance across the field, however, makes us realize with a shock that both the natural flowers and our blue decoys happen to be the darkest flower-like objects in the whole field. Was it darkness, irrespective of colour, that attracted the forager? Instead of flower-like decoys we put down paper squares of various shades of grey. There are available series of papers ranging from pure white to black via thirty shades of grey among which there is bound to be one which has the same luminosity as our blue decoy. We can combine all paper squares into a checker-board, putting one piece of our blue paper among them. We now find that as before the blue paper is visited, and all others ignored. In this way we can convince ourselves that blue is recognized as a colour. Similar experiments can be carried out to ascertain the range of colours that are specifically seen and recognized by this insect. In comparing various insects in this way and by more sophisticated experiments we find that insects differ quite considerably in the range of the hues they can see and distinguish. For instance, whereas bumble bees see red and distinguish it from other colours, the honey bee is red-blind. On the other hand, it can be shown that honey bees see ultraviolet of a wavelength to which the eye of the bumble bee and our own eyes are insensitive. The same holds for certain ants. A simple experiment can demonstrate this very elegantly.

A disturbed ants' nest is a fascinating thing to watch at all times. The excited coming and going of worker ants, seemingly purposeless, results nevertheless in ultimate order. Many of them can be seen to carry larvae at all stages of development, and their precious pupae, to a place of safety. This means to a dark place. After a time none of the vulnerable and defenceless brood is left exposed to the scrutiny of the intruder. This situation is tailor-made for an experiment. What if we keep an ants' nest in a dark room and illuminate it for the sake of observation with a red photographic safe-light. We now disturb the nest, and wait for developments. There is, of course, the usual commotion following upon the mechanical upheaval that must have the effect of an earthquake upon the ant community. Larvae and pupae are picked up as usual, but then they are quite readily deposited in full view of the observer somewhere in the open. One cannot help having the impression that for the ant the scene is one of disorder enveloped in total darkness. The ants are red-blind.

Now we proceed to the other end of the spectrum, switching off our red light and 'shining' a beam of ultraviolet 'light' on the nest. The inverted commas around 'shining' indicate that now we ourselves are in pitch darkness, because we cannot see ultraviolet of the chosen wavelength, say somewhere between 300 and 390 mμ. Presumably the ants keep on fetching and carrying and the effect of their efforts becomes clear, when after a while we switch back to our red safe-light again. Not a single grub or pupa has remained in the open, that is to say in a place exposed to the ultraviolet beams. Although leaving us in utter darkness, it must have produced the effect of broad daylight to the ants. They see ultraviolet. Other more sophisticated and better-controlled experiments confirm our conclusion. For bees and ants the visible part of the spectrum is shifted towards the ultraviolet end and away from the red.

We have so far used observation of spontaneous responses to selected sets of natural and artificial stimuli in our exploration of colour vision in animals. For more detailed analysis of the discriminatory powers of animals we have to resort to attempts at training them to respond to stimuli which they need not necessarily respond to in their day-to-day activities. One speaks of conditioning an animal by methods which were first worked out by the Russian physiologist Pavlov in his work on dogs. To show how such an experiment works and how it can give us information on an animal's colour vision we turn our attention to fish. Minnows have proved to be most useful for this purpose. They learn easily and retain what they have learned for long periods of time.

At first one may ask why fish should pay attention to colours. Do colours play any part in their aquatic environment? One has only to look at a male minnow during the breeding season, when its body becomes adorned with provocative coloured patches of red and green and silver, to see that colour vision would not be wasted on the females of the species, when they follow the courtship display of their male partners. But we are arguing this case backwards. Let us see whether minnows can see colours and distinguish them from one another. Tame minnows, which have learned to take food from a glass hook lowered into their aquarium, are fed on meat made colourless by soaking it in water. Now the hook carrying the meat is backed by a square piece of red plastic. It does not take the fish long to 'associate' red with food and they soon swim eagerly towards any red signal, whether there is a meat hook in front of it or not. However, blue or yellow signals of similar size and shape will also arouse the interest of the fish, and we suspect that the fish have really associated a signal as such with food rather than our red token colour. So we have to resort to some kind of mild punishment which we inflict whenever our minnow looks for food, for instance, in front of a blue instead of the red signal. The meat given in this case has been soaked in a bitter solution of quinine instead of water, and is therefore completely unpalatable. Again it does not take the minnow long to learn to ignore blue, or for that matter any other punitively baited colour signal. In this way one can demonstrate that minnows distinguish a certain red from a number of other colours of the spectrum and – very important indeed – from a grey of equal luminosity.

Colour-blind pets

If we use a similar technique on a cat or a dog we find that, however hard we try, we cannot make them distinguish coloured from uncoloured objects of the same size, shape, and luminosity. They appear to be totally colour-blind, like human monochromates. To them the world must appear as we see it on a black and white photograph. In fact, most mammals seem to be similarly devoid of colour vision. Why should that be so? There is a simple explanation that seems quite plausible. Most mammals are preponderantly active during dusk, at night, and at early dawn, when the world looks pretty grey even to man, with his highly developed appreciation of colours. Our study of mammalian colour vision is not by any means complete, but so far it seems that the Primates, to which we and the monkeys and apes belong, are the chief group of mammals equipped with colour vision. It is fairly certain, for instance, that the fighting-mad bull in the arena attacks a rag that does not appear red to him but black! Horses, too, don't seem to be able to enjoy their jockey's spectacular stable colours.

Quite a number of zoological gardens now illuminate the cages of small mammals with artificial 'moonlight', under which condition the inmates disport themselves with great liveliness instead of lying sleepily and hidden away in the ordinary daylight display cage. A glance at such a moonlit scene demonstrates how absolutely devoid of colour it is and how the black or brown and white markings of these mammals blend with the patchwork of light and shadow of their surroundings.

Table 1

Distribution of colour vision in the animal kingdom

ABSENT	DOUBTFUL	PRESENT
Many backbone-less animals	Some backboneless animals	Some lower back-boneless animals
Many lower fishes	Many lower fishes	Crustacea
Many amphibians	Many amphibians	Insects
Most mammals	Snakes	Bony fishes
	Crocodiles	Turtles
	Monotremes and marsupials	Lizards
	Some mammals	Birds
		Primate mammals

Table 1 shows the curious distribution of general colour vision in the animal kingdom; and a comparison between the range of colour vision of bee and man in particular is shown in Figure 13. It is clear that colour vision may have evolved in the various groups of animals alongside with coloration of their own bodies or of objects in their environment, the recognition and discrimination of which may be of survival value to them. Thus insects can be guided to food or protective shelter by the distinctive coloration of plants or other objects around them. The coloured plumage of birds plays an important part in courtship display. The luminous colours of deep-sea fish serve for recognition of friend or foe, and primitive man and his primate relatives may have derived great benefit from being able to distinguish an edible berry from a poisonous one of different colour. A glance at the vividly coloured faces or sit-upons of some male monkeys shows that here, too, colour may play its part in the relationship of the sexes. And as for civilized man – he has become truly addicted to colour.

So much, then, by way of a survey of colour vision as a natural phenomenon. Now we want to see how it is done.

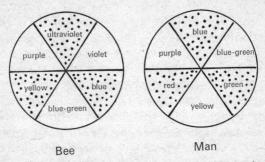

Bee   Man

Figure 13. This shows the colour circles of the honey bee and of man. The stippled sectors represent the primary colours, and the white areas represent the hues resulting from mixtures of them. It can be seen that in the bee the three primary colours, ultraviolet (UV), blue, and yellow, are shifted towards the short-wave end of the spectrum, as compared with the corresponding primary colours in man, viz. blue, green, and red. The bee's purple, which is a mixture of ultraviolet and yellow, is quite different in hue from our purple, which is a mixture of blue and red. (*Modified after Daumer.*)

The mechanism of colour vision

A child, after it has been given a water-colour set for Christmas, soon learns that a number of the blocks of pigment in the set are quite superfluous, and that it is much greater fun to obtain the desired hue by mixing some few selected colours. Yellow and blue in varying proportions yield shades of green; blue and red are favoured ingredients for purple or violet tints. Colour-printing in cheap magazines is often inaccurately superimposed and shows at the edge of the picture that its many-coloured effect has been achieved by printing a blue, a yellow, and a red copy on top of one another.

The laws of colour mixing have been known for quite a long time, but their use for an explanation of the mechanism of colour vision does not go back farther than the beginning of the nineteenth century, when Thomas Young for the first time stated quite clearly that light consists of a continuous series of what we would now call wavelengths of electromagnetic radiation, which he called 'kinds of light'. However, according to Young the eye itself possessed only three kinds of 'sensitive particle', each responding preferentially to light from a specific part of the spectrum. In fact, he assumed the presence in the retina of red-, yellow-, and blue-sensitive particles, but later changed this into red, green, and violet. It is essential here that we distinguish between colours reflected from paints or pigments on the one hand, and spectral colours obtained by diffraction of white light through a prism on the other. For our argument it will be easier to operate with spectral colours, if only because they can be produced in a relatively pure form (monochromatic light) and also link up directly with our knowledge of the electromagnetic spectrum. Colours of pigments are the result of subtraction from white light of all those wavelengths which the coloured substance absorbs, because of the constitution of its chemical ingredients. The situation here is therefore often very complex.

Primary colours and colour mixing

Three so-called primary colours can be isolated from the spectrum. They are red (650 mμ) and green (530 mμ) and blue (460 mμ). Equal quantities of the primary colours mixed together give white, but no mixture of two of them can produce the third. If we look at the spectrum as a whole we find that a mixture of two separate, but not too far distant, colours yields the intermediate one: e.g. yellow plus red yields orange. Their relative intensities push the colour of the mixture nearer to the brighter of the components. Two colours more distant from one another give a mixture which gets paler with increase of distance of the components, as if white were added to the intermediate hue. One speaks of unsaturation. Unsaturated red is pink, unsaturated orange becomes yellow. Yellow becomes green and green becomes yellow under such conditions; violet becomes salmon pink. Only yellow-green stays the same, and blue changes relatively little in hue on addition of white. When two hues are very far apart on the spectrum their mixture yields white. They are then called complementary colours such as red and green or yellow and blue.

The trichromatic theory of colour vision

Thomas Young postulated the presence in the retina of three kinds of 'sensitive particles', each for the reception of one primary colour. Translated into what we now know of the composition of the retina, this means that in a population of cones in the central area of the retina, where daylight vision is located, there may be some which are either exclusively or preferentially sensitive to red, others to green and others to blue or violet. When we look at the human retina we cannot discover three obviously different types of cone. They may all look alike, but may nevertheless contain different photosensitive pigments with specific absorbing powers in these three regions of the spectrum. So far it has not been possible to demonstrate three such pigments. The pigment we know best is visual purple or rhodopsin, which absorbs maximally at 500 mμ. Absorption falls off on either side of this peak. If we stimulate the peripheral parts of the retina, where the rods are chiefly situated, with a series of spectral colours ranging from

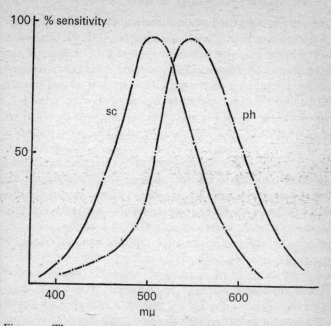

Figure 14. The two curves are plots of the sensitivity of the eye to a range of wavelengths of coloured light at various levels of illumination. In dim light the so-called scotopic sensitivity curve (sc) is obtained, whereas in bright light the eye yields the photopic curve (ph). The maximum sensitivity of the scotopic curve lies at 500 mμ, and that of the photopic curve at 560 mμ. The curves illustrate the effect described in the text. It is known as the Purkinje phenomenon. Sensitivities are plotted as percentage of maximum sensitivity.

red to violet and measure the sensitivity of the eye to each, when their absolute brightness is equal, we find that the sensitivity is highest to blue-green light of 500 mμ falling off on either side of this. A sensitivity curve plotted in this way will look very much like a curve on which the power of absorption of rhodopsin for the various wavelengths is plotted. Under such conditions, within a range of dim illumination compatible with the high absolute sensitivity of the rods, the observer does not see any colour, but only varying brightness, despite the fact that coloured lights are being used in the experiments. In broad daylight, however, a different sensitivity curve is obtained, with a peak of sensitivity at 560 mμ, the yellow region of the spectrum (Figure 14).

The question of specific pigments

In this experiment the observer sees the different spectral colours, but their brightness decreases on either side of the peak despite the fact that the colours offered are adjusted to have the same absolute energy content. The so-called photopic sensitivity curve must represent the sum total of the sensitivities of our postulated three types of cone receptors. It would be scientifically desirable if the trichromatic or three-receptor theory of vision could be verified by the discovery of three different pigments. The absorption curves of these should then fit snugly into the area under the photopic curve. Work has been done with colour-blind observers and normal subjects, including measurements of light absorption by direct inspection of the illuminated retina. Dr Rushton at Cambridge used this technique and found some evidence for the existence of at least two specialized photo-pigments differing in their absorption curves from visual purple. A green-sensitive pigment, 'chlorolable', is found in the fovea of the eyes of protanopes, and the fovea of people with normal colour vision contains in addition a red-sensitive pigment called 'erythrolable'. A specifically blue-sensitive pigment has only very recently been measured in the human retina. The question whether chlorolable and erythrolable are two of the three pigments necessary for a trichromate mechanism of colour vision cannot be answered yet with any degree of confidence. It is true, quite a series of different visual pigments have been isolated in animals, and often their absorption spectra fit in well with environmental requirements. However, one has to be careful not to jump to conclusions about their role in colour vision, as even the properties of ordinary rod pigments can vary quite considerably in different animal species.

When talking of rod and cone pigments, one must not forget that the difference between these two types of receptor is almost insignificant in some animals. In man the cones don't look as different from the rods as they do, for instance, in a fish. There are animals in which all retinal receptors look like rods, or others which have a so-called pure cone retina. In short, the problems of colour vision are far from being solved, and quite surprising new facts may 'come to light' that may revolutionize our ideas. Nevertheless, for a time it looked as if the evidence for the existence of three different kinds of foveal receptors, each sensitive over a narrow range of wavelengths only, was pretty conclusive.

Electrophysiological evidence

The Swedish physiologist Ragnar Granit had been able to record different sensory impulses from units of the cat retina, and these responses were highly specific for three narrow ranges of wavelength in the red, green, and blue region of the spectrum. He called these sensory units modulators and it was thought that they could be connected with three different sensory cells in the retina, although the active impulses were picked up not from the cones themselves but from ganglion cells in the ganglionic layer of the retina (see Figure 9, p. 46). That such units should exist in the retina of an animal like the cat, which is almost certainly colour-blind, was interpreted in the following way. It was said that the cat may in fact have the complete retinal machinery for colour discrimination, but may, as a nocturnal animal, never have had any necessity to make use of 'chromatic information'. Consequently, the central nervous system may not have evolved a computing system responsible for 'conjuring up' the experience of colour. Since, however, the sensitivity curves of Granit's modulators are too narrow to fit in with the absorption curves of known pigments, the significance of his discoveries cannot yet be fully assessed.

A new hypothesis

The whole question of colour vision is still wide open. This is driven home most forcefully by the fact that a completely new way of looking at the whole matter has recently been proposed by Arthur Land, who is known to the general public as the inventor of the polaroid camera which delivers a fully finished positive print of a snapshot immediately after taking. Land has investigated the fact that the relative brightness to our eye of quiltwork patterns of black, greys, and white is independent of the overall intensity and uniformity of illumination. Starting out from these observations he went on to consider the constancy of colours under widely different conditions of illumination in similar quiltwork patterns made up from many different colours. We all experience this when we look at a natural outdoor scene – say a rose garden – and a cloud moves over the sun. Although the whole view may darken, the colours remain the same. Land postulates the existence in the visual system – that is in the retina plus the optical centres of the brain – of a mechanism of assessing relative brightness independent of the absolute amount of light energy reflected from objects. So far as colour vision is concerned, it is thought that there may be three quite independent computers of this kind working in the long-, middle-, and short-wave range of the spectrum, and that the sensation of colour may be the result of the comparison of different orders of brightness in the three different ranking systems. Land calls each such system a 'retinex'. Thus a certain colour may be characterized by the index 2, 4, 3 in the long-, middle-, and short-wave retinex respectively. Such a theory is not incompatible with the existence of three different kinds of receptors or visual pigment, but is claimed to simplify the interpretation of a number of puzzling observations on colour vision. The following is an example of such a puzzling case.

A startling experiment

Two black and white lantern-slides are taken of the same coloured objects, the one taken through a green, the other through a red filter in front of the camera lens. Obviously the two views will differ drastically in the distribution of light and shade. If they are now projected by two identical projectors in such a way that the outlines of objects register accurately on the screen, and if the slide taken through a green filter is projected straight, and the other through a red filter, one would expect the picture of the scene to be composed of various shades of pink. Not at all. The picture on the screen is coloured to a certain extent and may show greys, browns, reds, blues, greens, purples, and so on! All this despite the fact that the only obvious colour offered to the eye is the red of the filter in front of one of the two projectors. A detailed explanation for this can be derived from Land's retinex hypothesis. It would go too far here to follow this through, and the matter is mentioned only to show how little settled our views on colour vision still are.

Our range of colours

Normal man has a highly discriminative sense for colour and distinguishes a great number of hues and grades of broken colour. There exist comprehensive standard works on the science and aesthetics of colour, among them so-called colour dictionaries. In such a work we may find over thirty standard hues, each of which may yield three 'tints' if mixed with varying amounts of white and three shades if mixed with black. If we add to this broken colours which are full colours mixed with grey and use adjectives such as light, medium, dark, saturated, weak, vivid, pale, dusky, deep, we can arrive at over three hundred items in a colour catalogue.

It is fascinating to see how the number of names for different colours varies in various languages and language groups, and even among professional groups using the same language. In everyday English we distinguish basically between purple, blue, green, yellow, orange, and red. The Shona, a native tribe in Rhodesia, have only three colour names in their vocabulary, other tribes have only two. We need not go to Africa to find a group of people using only two colour terms. The botanists subdivide flower colours into cyanic and xanthic (blue- and yellow-tinted). This gives us the key to the apparent poverty of some vocabularies. Colour names in such cases are collective names each covering a range of colours, within which distinctions of hue may or may not be made by qualifying adjectives such as poppy-red or cornflower-blue. The old Anglo-Saxons were apparently more interested in brightness than in colour, hence their frequent allusion to gleaming, shadowy, lowering. Sea-waves, the sword-edge, or a helmet would all be 'brun'. 'Wan' was dull, 'dun' was sallow. Only in later writing do green and red appear with connotations of hue. In old English poetry blue is practically nonexistent. Violet and orange, which by the way are both descriptive of natural objects, were also absent from the vocabulary in which green, red, and yellow were almost the only colour names. The Romans had words for dark or murky, for chestnut colours, for golden-brown, and even the word 'rubidus', usually translated as red, covered the range between red and black. All this has made people think that maybe colour vision as we know it emerged in historical times. We can, however, be reasonably sure that the proportion of colour-blind to normal people has not altered much. Different civilizations focus a different amount of interest on colour and appreciation of hue grows in proportion to needs.

4

INFRA-RED AND BEYOND

Infra-red sensitivity

THE visible spectrum ends at a wavelength of 700 mμ on the red side. The range beyond this is known as infra-red. Photographic film and plates are made which are sensitive to infrared. Photographs of landscapes and other objects taken on such plates look very strange indeed. For instance, a mountain range completely invisible on a hazy day and not showing up at all on an ordinary photograph appears clear in all its details on an infra-red one. The long-wave infra-red rays reflected from the mountain range, to which our eye and ordinary film are blind, penetrate much better through haze than shorter-wave light. On aerial reconnaissance photographs taken at night, the most carefully blacked-out cities show up on infra-red plates because of the greater amount of infra-red rays emitted by relatively warmer built-up areas than by the surrounding countryside.

What makes an electric radiator so agreeable to us when coming home from a walk in cold and damp weather is not the visible red glow of the element – although this helps by an ingrained association of ours between redness and warmth. No – our comfort is derived from the infra-red heat rays which we do not see. Do we then feel them? The answer is only indirectly. We do not appear to possess any sensory structures that are directly sensitive to this part of the electromagnetic spectrum. The fact is that these rays are absorbed by the tissues of our skin and in this way are transformed into 'warmth', which we perceive with the aid of temperature receptors (to be described in Chapter 5).

It has puzzled naturalists quite a lot how some snakes can

locate a mouse or rat sitting absolutely still in absolute darkness and quite a distance away from the reptile. When the snake strikes, it hardly ever fails to hit the target. Distance and direction of the strike are uncannily correct. Could it be that such a snake can see and accurately locate its prey in absolute darkness, when the only radiation emanating from it would be

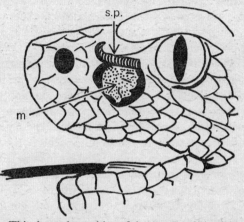

Figure 15. This shows the position of the sensory pit (s.p.) in the head of a pit viper. The pit organ lies between nose and eye and is here exposed by removal of some of the surrounding tissue. The folded membrane (stippled) contains the nerve endings sensitive to radiant heat. (*Modified after Bullock and Diecke.*)

infra-red heat rays of greater intensity than those coming from the ground and background? There is no evidence that the snake's eye differs in this way from eyes of other backboned animals. Or could it be a very acute power of hearing and localizing sound direction far surpassing anything known in other animals? Again the answer is no. Snakes don't hear airborne sound well, and to locate so accurately by sound perception through the ground would be a remarkable achievement for the tactile sense.

A clue towards the solution of this problem comes from investigations on rattle-snakes or pit vipers which are known to be able to locate and strike a sitting prey in darkness. The rattle-snake has a pair of so-called pit organs situated in front of its eyes (Figure 15). These are, like the eyes, symmetrically placed on either side of the head. Each has a fairly wide opening pointing forward. There is an empty cavity, the rear wall of which consists of a thin sheet of tissue richly supplied with nerve endings. If both pits are plugged or their openings covered over, the snake fails to locate prey in the dark. It is not too difficult to make electrical recordings from the nerves supplying the organ, and it can be shown that chemical and mechanical stimulation and visible light do not produce striking responses. Quite different effects are obtained when one directs infra-red heat rays into the pit. These produce a lively discharge of nerve impulses in the sensory nerve fibres and the sensitivity is very high indeed, as high in fact as the direct warming of the membrane at the base of the pit by means of a warm object put in contact with it.

The possibility therefore exists that there are in these membranes specialized receptor cells for the selective absorption of infra-red electromagnetic radiation. A human hand at a distance of 2 to 3 feet from the pit – or an object of a temperature 1° Centigrade higher or lower than its surroundings held close to the pit – will produce a significant change in the electric activity of the nerve fibres. It is sufficient for an object to be either warmer or colder than its immediate surroundings to excite this sense organ even if the object's temperature is the same as that of the snake. There are geometrical relationships in the positioning and shape of the pits which explain the fact that the snake can 'estimate' distance as well as direction of the source of infra-red radiation. Experiments with filters and with artificial sources of infra-red radiation have shown that the organ is most sensitive to the long infra-red rays of wavelengths between 2 and 3 μ, even up to 10 and 15 μ. These are five to twenty times longer than the wavelength of red light and lie, in fact, well within the range of wavelengths emitted by a warm animal of prey, or for that matter by a human hand. The actual mechanism of transduction is unlikely to involve a photochemical reaction of the kind found in the light-sensitive receptors in the eye. The energy content of these long waves is not high enough for this. However, there are organic substances which are known to absorb long-wave infra-red specifically and such absorption was, at first, thought to be responsible for the transduction process. On the other hand, the absorption may be general rather than wavelength specific. This is pretty complicated biophysics and we can at present only guess. It is interesting that so far this sort of organ has been studied only in these rattle-snakes, and the question remains open whether other animals that have to find their way about in the dark may be found to have similar infra-red receptors.

In man no such organs are known, although there may exist a less geometrically localized general skin sensitivity to infrared radiation to which we normally don't pay attention, but which may become important in the blind, who claim to get better warning of obstacles if their foreheads are bare and not covered by a hat.

Infra-red radiation can, of course, be utilized in orientation by means of so-called image converters. These are gadgets in which infra-red is converted into visible light, so that the distribution of infra-red patterns can be made visible. Such apparatus was used in the war in night convoys when headlights had to be switched off. Thus, as usual, man has been able to make up by his inventiveness for the short-comings in his sensory equipment.

There are a number of possible sources of information inaccessible to us which are utilized by animals. Let us return to the realm of visible light. Electromagnetic waves may be described as oscillations propagated in a straight line. If we imagine a wave bundle oscillating at a certain frequency, the question arises whether its oscillation is up and down, from right to left or diagonal. In fact, normally the plane of oscillation in a light beam changes direction continuously, rotating full circle. If such a beam is intercepted by a structure such as a certain crystal which allows passage for light oscillating in one plane only, we find that the light transmitted by such a filter is 'polarized' in that plane. It only oscillates up and down or horizontally or at a certain angle. The light from a blue cloudless sky is polarized in this way and the angle of polarization depends on the compass direction with relation to the position of the sun.

We now know that there are quite a number of animals, especially among the insects and other arthropods such as crabs and shrimps, that can actually visually distinguish light polarized in one direction from light of a different plane of polarization, and that they can use this information in 'navigating'. That the honey bee can do this explains its remarkable power of 'steering by the sun'. We do not know yet for certain which structure in the compound eye acts as an analyser for polarized light, but there is reason to suspect that the arrangement of retinula cells in the ommatidium may have something to do with this. Our own eyes and those of our fellow vertebrates appear to be unable to make use of the directional information derived from differences in polarization of light waves.

The long-wave end of the electromagnetic spectrum

The electromagnetic spectrum extends of course far beyond the infra-red spectrum. There is the range of so-called wireless waves from the ultrashort, or very high frequency (V.H.F.), via short waves and medium waves to the long waves on the dials of our radio sets. We make use of these in radio-communication by modulating them with signals which a radio or television set transduces into sound or into the visible pattern on a television screen. We cannot, however, 'sense' these waves unaided by any special gadget. And this may be just as well. It may be said that animals in general ought not to be expected to react to radio waves, because these do not make up part of their natural environment, transmitted as they are by man-made radio stations. However, all 'radio' waves are not man-made. Stars, among them many dark ones known as radio stars, and other cosmic objects send out electromagnetic waves of this kind which can now be received by radio telescopes, by means of which an enormous amount of new information about the universe has fairly recently 'come to light'. What is more, any electric discharge such as lightning can give rise to electromagnetic waves.

Electric fields

There are quite a number of aquatic animals capable of discharging electric shocks and pulses into the surrounding water. So-called electric fish have organs consisting of modified muscles in which the electric potentials across their cell membranes are accumulated in such a way as to make them capable of discharging shocks of quite considerable voltage that can stun or even kill enemies or prey. Electric eels can deliver most painful and even stunning shocks on handling. Quite a number of fish have less-powerful electric organs, by means of which they send out series of electric pulses while they swim about.

It has recently been discovered that these pulses are used in orientation. What happens is this. Each of the electric pulses discharged by the electric organ generates an electric field around it, with a gradient of decreasing voltage extending from the centre of discharge somewhere in the body of the fish, to the surrounding water. It has to be emphasized that we are now speaking of *electric fields* and not of electromagnetic waves. Objects that differ in their power to conduct electricity

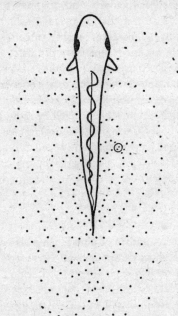

Figure 16. This shows an electric fish surrounded by its electric field symbolized by the dotted lines of equal potential. The typically undulating dorsal fin is the chief locomotory organ in these fish, which swim without the usual sideways movement of body and tail. In this way the electric field can spread in all directions undisturbed by body movement. Near the right flank of the fish a circular body of higher electrical conductivity than the surrounding water is seen to distort the electric field. It must be assumed that the fish can sense the disturbance and accurately locate the centre of distortion. (*Modified after Lissman*.)

from that of the surrounding water will distort the electric fields emanating from the pulsing organ (Figure 16). We now assume that the electric fish does not only generate electricity but has also sense organs responding to changes in the electric potential near the body surface of the fish. Distortion of the emitted field results in such changes in electric potential, and this can be 'sensed' in such a way as to enable the fish to localize the object whose higher or lower conductivity causes the disturbance. This sounds like a tall story, and it must be confessed that so far we don't know an awful lot about the sense organs responding to changes in electric potential. The fact remains, however, that fish sending out electric pulses have been observed to locate accurately a piece of iron hidden in the mud by means of their power to sense the distortion of the electric field generated by these pulses. Of course, fish don't naturally hunt for old iron – but any object such as another fish or any prey that influences the field can be equally well located. Obviously, such sense organs will certainly be stimulated by pulses sent out by another electric fish, and one can be sure that electric fish can communicate in this way. It is quite easy to convert such pulses into sound blips by inserting an electrode into the water and connecting it with an amplifier and loudspeaker. One then hears the more or less rapid series of pulses emitted by the 'electric' fish. This goes on all the time while the fish swims about, but especially when it is agitated in any way, which is shown by a great increase in pulse frequency. Such a demonstration is very striking, and is one of the attractions in public aquaria where electric fish are kept.

I was privileged to witness one of the earliest experiments in which it was shown that fish are sensitive to outside electric fields, and it was not a coincidence that this concerned the electric eel *Gymnotus electricus*. It happened in 1932. The animal, which at rest likes to hide between rocks, was kept in an aquarium with a large earthenware drainpipe provided as a hiding-place. The animal was being trained to respond to sound in the course of an investigation of its hearing power (see Chapter 7). As a source of sound an electric oscillator was used for the production of pure notes, and provision had been made for the sounding of the notes without any other disturbance, such as the clicking of switches. The apparatus was brought near the tank while the fish was in hiding, and this could be done without arousing the fish. The fish was being trained to come out of its drainpipe and search for food whenever a particular note was sounded. This was achieved. But after a while the fish made its appearance whenever the set was switched on, even without a note being sounded. It was thought that the animal had learned to react to the low humming noise of the transformer, but this factor could be eliminated by control experiments. Then the suspicion arose that the fish might be sensitive to the electric field emanating from the oscillator. Two large metal plates were now erected on either side of the tank and these were connected with the oscillator, which had been removed to an adjoining room. Although, now, the transformer noise was no longer audible, the fish reacted strongly when the oscillator was switched on. The same happened when the metal plates were connected to the a.c. mains.

A possible direct effect of electromagnetic radio waves on animals has been postulated in migrating birds, whose orientation during homing was suspected to be disturbed in the vicinity of the antennae of powerful radio stations. But this has so far not been reliably disproved or proved.

Magnetic fields

Sensitivity of animals to pure magnetic fields of considerable strength is at present being investigated, especially after it has been shown that such fields can influence growth and development of plants. Orientation of homing pigeons was for a time also thought to be guided by the earth's magnetic field, but this idea was given up when it could be shown that homing was not upset by permanent magnets tied to the birds' wings, although such magnets should have disturbed the geo-magnetic field considerably.

We are in this matter clearly standing at the border of yet unexplored realms of sense perception, and the future may reveal interesting and unthought-of faculties in animals. It is unavoidable that one's thoughts should, in this connexion, turn to E.S.P. or extrasensory perception. We shall deal with this matter in the last chapter.

5

MECHANORECEPTORS I

The skin as a sense organ

IT is a cherished habit of the Englishman to carry his small change loose in his trouser pocket. This gives him, day in and day out, an opportunity to test the skill of his fingertips in sorting out coins of different sizes and shapes by touch alone. The use of a public telephone box calls for the choice of a hexagonal threepenny bit, at the newspaper stall it may be a matter of finding out four pennies individually from among florins and half-crowns. It is astonishing what complex sensory mechanisms are involved in these routine performances of the tactile sense. When it comes to a blind person reading braille by the fleeting scanning of complex patterns of raised points with the fingertips, we reach a degree of tactile sensitivity and discrimination that makes us curious to find out about the sensory structures responsible for the 'picking up' and processing of this type of sensory information.

A fingertip under the microscope

When we look at a piece of skin from the human fingertip under the microscope, we find that the second-outer layer or dermis is richly supplied with thin end-branches of skin nerves (Figure 17). These run in between the connective-tissue cells of the dermis and overlap, like the branches of trees in a dense forest, so that the endings of each skin nerve cover a certain area of skin, each area receiving end-branches from a number of neighbouring stems. The skin nerves run through the underlying tissues and unite to form the sensory part of the nerve supply of the hand and arm with the sensory neurons in the dorsal root of the spinal cord as their final destination. In the spinal cord, processes from these neurons make contact with the nerve tracts leading to the tactile areas of the brain.

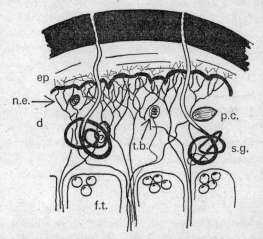

Figure 17. This is a highly diagrammatic representation of a section through the skin of our fingertip. The horny layer (black) of the epidermis (ep) is pierced by the ducts from two sweat glands (s.g.). Embedded in the connective tissue of the dermis (d) is the web-work of interlacing tactile nerve endings (n.e.), some of which are organized into more complex tactile bodies (t.b.). A Pacinian corpuscle (p.c.) can be seen among them. Below the dermis lie parcels of fatty tissue (f.t.). The finest ramifications of the tactile fibres cannot be shown on this scale. Their ends are frequently coiled up into skeins with or without connective tissue cover. A web-work of endings penetrate into the epidermis, where they are spun round the cells of the lower layers.

The whole system of nerve supply to the fingertips looks so haphazard that it is difficult to see how the exact whereabouts of the touch stimulus on the surface of the fingertip can be so accurately assessed as to give a minute tactile image of the explored object. The very fact that we use the term tactile image shows how well satisfied our visually orientated imagination can be by this type of sensory information. Indeed, in a blind person, it has to replace visual information, and can do so to an astonishing degree.

Figure 18 shows how the pinpointing of the exact spot of stimulation may be signalled to the nervous system. There are processes of three different neurons distributed over a small

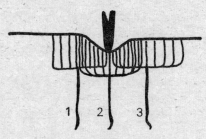

Figure 18. This shows highly diagrammatically how the end-branches of three tactile nerve fibres in the human skin (see Figure 17) are affected by a deformation of the skin. Six branches of nerve 2 are stimulated – some of them maximally – whereas only four of nerve 1 and three of nerve 3 become involved. How this serves in pinpointing the tactile stimulus is discussed in the text.

area of the skin, and they overlap in the way indicated. Let us now assume that a deformation of the skin, however slight, sets up in the nerve endings the electric events which lead to the firing of a train of nerve impulses. Again we assume that the number of impulses per second or the firing rate is proportional to the intensity of the tactile stimulus, or better to say in our case, to the degree of deformation of the skin and the nerve endings in it. One further assumption is that the analysing centre can 'discriminate' between the signals coming from fibre 1, 2, 3, and so on, and that they are represented in the centre in their relative positions like geographical features on a map.

A stimulus, say the contact with the fingertip of the point of a bristle, will stimulate maximally the end-branches of nerve fibre 2, but owing to the overlap it will also affect the endings of nerves 1 and 3, but not so strongly. The computing cells at the centre appear to be able to distinguish between these impulse patterns, and we know, with our eyes closed, the exact spot on our fingertip touched by the bristle.

This is a very oversimplified situation, but it is intended to illustrate the principle of localization of tactile stimuli. Instead of three nerve fibres, patterns of the endings from hundreds of fibres may be involved in any case. Furthermore, not all fibres have the same sensitivity, and they may differ widely in quickness of uptake, frequency, range of response, or in the way in which they adapt or settle down under prolonged stimulation. If these properties are, so to speak, registered within central analysing stations, there will be ample scope for the most refined analysis and conscious presentation of all manner of tactile stimuli, from a fleeting tickle to continued contact. We distinguish well between slight touch and pressure. Strong pressure may become disagreeable and bring about the sensation of pain. A cut and a bruise feel differently, and so does a burn. Hot and cold produce quite different sensations. It is not surprising, therefore, that one has looked out in the skin for specific nerve endings for the various types of mechanical stimulation. It may not be immediately obvious that, heat being physically a matter of motion, hot and cold are due to different degrees of mechanical agitation of the skin tissue and its nerve endings.

Specialized nerve endings

In fact, not all nerve endings look alike under the microscope, and it was thought that there were as many different types of them as there are different kinds of mechanical stimulus. For instance, two types of coiled endings were described as hot and cold receptor endings respectively. Other coiled endings lying in the deeper layers of the skin and being surrounded by a group of specialized skin cells were thought to be specifically pressure sensitive. Most elaborate of all are the so-called Pacinian bodies, in which a thin straight nerve ending is

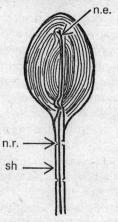

Figure 19. This is a highly magnified view of a Pacinian corpuscle from the diaphragm. The nerve ending (n.e.) can be seen to be encapsulated by a system of concentric membranes. The nerve emerging from the corpuscle is covered by a fatty nerve sheath (sh) with its nodes of Ranvier (n.r.).

ensheathed in concentric layers of connective tissue, forming an elliptic capsule (Figure 19). They are known to be sensitive to pressure, and to give an idea of their sensitivity it was found experimentally that a compression of 1/2,000 mm. in 1/10 millisecond produces a noticeable impulse response. The function of the capsule is not fully understood. It may give protection to a highly sensitive nerve ending, or it may transfer the mechanical stimulus to it in a certain direction, as it may alter by its elasticity the time course of the response.

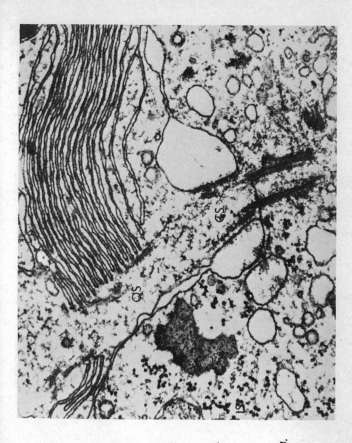

Plate 1
High-magnification
electron-microscopic
view of a stack of
membranes in the
developing rod of the
tadpole eye. Note the
ciliary root in the
connecting structure
(c.s.) between the
outer segment (o.s.)
and the inner segment
(i.s.) of the rod.
Magnification
approximately ×38,000.
(Compare Figure 8.)

*From: S. E. G. Nilsen,
J. Ultrastructure
Research Volume 11,
581, Academic Press, 1964.*

Plate 2
The head of an
African Longhorn
Beetle, showing
compound eyes. Note
the numerous facets
of the individual
ommatidia. (Compare
Figure 11.)

Plate 3
Rattlesnake about to
strike. The pit organ
lies between the nostril
and the eye. (Compare
Figure 15.)

*Reproduced by kind
permission of Dr R. A.
Boolootian, Department
of Zoology, University
of California, Los Angeles.*

Plate 4
Two 'electric' fishes
(*Mormyridae*).

*From: Url Lanham,
The Fishes (Plate 16),
Columbia University
Press, 1962.*

With an incredibly delicate technique it has been possible to peel away the capsule membrane from an isolated Pacinian corpuscle while recording the impulse response from its nerve in response to pressure applied to the capsule. It was found that all membranes could be removed in this way without abolishing or damaging the response.

The distribution of Pacinian corpuscles in the body is interesting. They are found in the lower layers of the skin of the fingertips, and in the soles of our feet, but also in the diaphragm and the connective tissues in which the gut is suspended. In birds they are found on the sinews of the legs. It is clear, therefore, that according to where they are situated they may serve to signal a variety of mechanical stimuli, giving rise to sensations ranging from touch and pressure to pain, and there is some evidence that they may be sensitive vibration receptors. It has been possible to teach deaf-mutes to dance to gramophone music, and it is believed that among the receptors through which they become aware of the beat of the music are the Pacinian corpuscles in their diaphragm. They may therefore literally hear with their tummies! Another intriguing fact remains that some tissues, like the cornea of the eye, are sensitive to touch, pressure, hot, and cold, and yet do not contain any of the complex types of nerve endings.

When we started our study of the tactile sense we were fumbling in our pocket for a coin, and considered how we recognized it without looking. Touch and pressure sensations were utilized in this feat. However, in the exploration of the coin's surface, its size too was recognized, and distinguished from that of others. This was not achieved by fingertip touch alone. The degree of bending of the fingers around the coin and the distance between the fingers holding it were accurately signalled to the central computing station by yet another set of mechanoreceptors located in the finger joints. We shall deal with them in the next chapter.

Our fingertips are covered with smooth skin continuous with that of the palm of the hand. The back of our hand is covered with hairy skin, and we need only stroke it gently to realize how the hairs heighten tactile sensitivity. Indeed, each hair is a

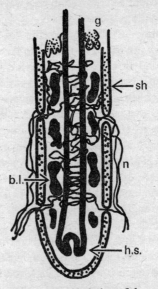

Figure 20. This is a highly magnified view of the root of a tactile hair. Nerve fibres (n) are seen to penetrate the hair sheath (sh) and to surround the hair shaft (h.s.). Two grease glands (g) are shown at the top and a number of blood lacunae (b.l.) are seen to surround the hair shaft. They act as elastic pads against which the nerve fibres are pressed when the hair bends. Bending of the hair is signalled to the central nervous system and conveys information on tactile stimulation.

tactile outpost and registers the slightest bending of its shaft. Blow gently against the palm of your hand first and then just as gently at the back of your hand, or any other area of hairy skin, and you will become conscious of the difference in sensitivity. Figure 20 shows how the root of a hair is entwined in a

skein of nerve fibres. They are compressed or deformed whenever the long lever of the hair shaft is moved in its socket.
The hair vibrating in the gentle stream of air evokes a sensation of tickle. The tickle is a quality of tactile sensation quite
different from touch and pressure, and the origin of this
difference is not yet well understood in terms of sensory
receptors and transmission.

Pain

Another province of the mechanical sense still full of unsolved
problems is pain. The baffling nature of pain becomes strikingly clear when one considers the reports of patients who have
lost a limb by amputation, but can still feel and localize so-
called phantom pain in a finger or toe of the long-lost limb.
It is clear that free nerve endings must be chiefly involved in
the reception of painful stimuli, because pain is registered by
parts of the body exclusively supplied by them. On the other
hand, it is well known that in the last resort all sensory structures can evoke painful sensations on overstimulation. This is
true for eye and ear as well as for skin receptors. In the skin
it is thought that a particularly thin type of free nerve ending
is set aside for the receptor of damaging stimuli, and for the
setting in motion of the biologically so very important warning
device of pain. We shall come back to the sense of pain in
Chapter 10.

Temperature receptors

Hot and cold sensations can also reach painful dimensions,
but let us see how temperature is registered within normal
limits. Can temperature be accurately assessed at all? One
rather doubts this when one remembers that time-honoured
experiment, in which an observer is asked to immerse the
left hand in ice-cold and the right hand in hot water. Transfer
of one or the other hand into water of room temperature evokes

two opposite sensations. To the left hand the same water appears wonderfully warm, to the right hand chillingly cold. Neither hand assesses the temperature of the test basin accurately. This relativity of heat sensation has led to the assumption that a proper temperature sense does not exist, and that all we can register are changes in temperature. This is a complex problem and we cannot do it justice here. Nevertheless, animals with a fairly constant body temperature, to whom we ourselves belong, appear to have separate sense endings for hot and cold, or, better to say, for hotter and colder than our body. Responses from such sense endings have been recorded oscillographically, and it is immaterial for our argument whether they were specialized coiled endings, or just specially attuned free nerve endings. It was found that there are nerve fibres in the skin that fire at a maximum rate at a temperature well above, and others at a temperature well below the normal body temperature, 98·4° Fahrenheit. It is obvious that local changes of skin temperature will affect these two types of nerve ending differently. The one will increase its activity on warming up (heat receptor), the other on cooling down (cold receptor) from body temperature. In this simple manner, changes in local skin temperature can be very accurately signalled to the central nervous system.

The cause of heating or cooling of the skin may be contact with a hot or cold body, or the exposure to a warm or cold air-stream, or the warming of the skin by radiant heat from an electric fire. In all these cases the receptor ending reacts to the temperature change in the skin tissues surrounding it. In Chapter 4 the possibility has been discussed that some animals such as rattle-snakes may have sense organs capable of registering infra-red electromagnetic radiation directly, so to speak pseudo-optically, without the mediation of warming or cooling of body tissues. It will, however, be remembered that the evidence for this is hardly satisfactory.

6

MECHANORECEPTORS II

Automation

IF we wanted to design a two-legged robot-man walking up-right, one of the difficulties we would have to overcome would be to keep it from toppling over. We would have to equip it with automatic controls for the maintenance of the upright posture or for its return to it after bending down. It must not be allowed to deviate too much from the vertical during its lumbering progress, and the movements of 'body and limbs' must be restrained within their proper operational limit by preventing 'overshoot'. In fact, such robots have been designed and so-called 'sensors' for the control of posture and movement make up the most costly part of the mechanism.

It would be a feather in the cap for biologists if we could honestly say that the know-how for this constructional task could fundamentally have been gained from the knowledge of how all this works in our own body. Alas, this is not so. The engineers have beaten us to it, and many devices to be incorporated in our robot will be modifications of gyro-stabilizers used in ships, or gun-laying mechanisms developed especially for tanks, but also for naval guns, and from predictors for anti-aircraft guns.

Many of these gadgets work on the principle of automatic feedback. This principle is applied in its simplest form in the automatic steam-valve regulator of steam engines. The steam pressure in the boiler adjusts itself to optimum level by raising a heavily weighted lever, which gives vent to the escape of superfluous steam when the pressure is too high, and closes the escape valve tightly when the pressure has been reduced to safe operational levels. In a mobile steam engine this mechanism can be combined with a centrifugal fly-wheel coupled with the road wheels. This is adjusted to raise the escape valve when the desired maximum speed is exceeded. The fly-wheel is the 'sensor' providing the power plant with a feedback of information about the success of its efforts. In this case we have negative feedback because the information is used for the throttling of the power output. In other cases a sensor may initiate the increase in power output, when we would be dealing with a positive feedback mechanism.

When at last the biologists came to grips with the analysis of similar coordinating mechanisms in the animal body, they were greatly helped both intellectually and practically by the consideration of such principles as evolved in engineering. As was pointed out in Chapter 2 (p. 33), the shoe begins to be worn on the other foot, and it is hoped that the results of bionics research are going to fertilize engineering design to an ever-increasing degree. It may be said that, after all, man is not a robot, and therefore all this automatic gadgetry may be very little relevant to our understanding of postural and movement control. Nothing would be farther from the truth. As will be seen presently, the coordination of limb movement and body posture is almost entirely unconscious and automatic, and however complex the sensory structures involved, the information issuing from them hardly ever reaches the higher centres of the brain, but gives rise to what the biologist calls reflex reactions. A word or two about the nature of reflex actions may be helpful.

The reflex arc

When at a crowded cocktail party the back of my hand comes up against somebody's lighted cigarette, the sequence of events is: first a very rapid withdrawal of the hand, then his or her muttered apology, then my 'not-at-all', and perhaps at that time the thought – yes, really it hurts, and a quick look at the red spot which then begins to smart.

The rapid withdrawal of the hand was done unconsciously and much more rapidly than it could have been done deliberately. In fact, the nervous pathway from the overstimulated spot of skin to somewhere in the nervous system and back to the muscles which executed the withdrawal movements involved only a few nerve cells and their processes, and was never linked up with the brain at all. This is what the physiologists call a reflex pathway or reflex arc. The central nervous exchange station between incoming sensory information and outgoing motor command is the spinal cord.

It is by such reflexes that posture and movement are controlled. The sensory outposts involved are manifold. In Chapter 5 we considered the tactile function of the skin with its sensory nerve endings for the registration of touch and pressure stimuli. Quite obviously such organs are also capable of providing information about the way the various parts of our limbs are held and move relative to one another. As I bend my forearm upwards to scratch the tip of my nose – I can do so blindfolded or in pitch-darkness without missing the target; in other words, I 'know' where my arm is throughout the movement – the skin of my arms near the elbow folds during the flexure of the joint and I feel this. Moreover, there are mechanoreceptors in the joint capsule itself which signal the changes of pressure and stress in the capsule to the appropriate central nervous stations. How far these first outposts report to the brain is not quite known, but we are no doubt able to focus attention on this process and consciously visualize the position of our arm in space at any given time. During the bustle of normal activity, however, we are not aware of all this in the same way as we look at the road ahead. Of course, movements of body and limbs can be controlled visually by watching the limb in question, and this is done as a matter of course by patients suffering from a malfunction of the postural sensory mechanism. In such cases it can be seen how tardy and awkward conscious control of movement can be. The control of movement and posture through sense organs in skin and joints is known as kinesthetic control (from the Greek for movement and feeling). The great physiologist Sherrington coined the term proprioceptive for such mechanisms, meaning '*receiving*' information about what happens in *ourselves*. He was mainly concerned with sensory structures in the muscles and joints. It is now quite clear that the messages from muscle receptors don't ordinarily reach our consciousness. We, therefore, prefer to speak of them as stretch receptors.

Stretch receptors

Let us then have a look at a limb muscle or at a muscle involved in the movement of our neck. The function of a muscle is to change its length by contraction or relaxation in accordance with nervous commands reaching it in the form of electric impulses from the command parts in the spinal cord or brain. Figure 21 shows a small sliver of muscle and it is seen that this consists of a number of parallel fibres which show a distinct cross-striation. This striation is intimately concerned with the minute structure of each muscle fibre and with the mechanism of contraction and relaxation. The analysis of this is a thrilling story by itself, but it lies outside our inquiry.

It will be seen that three of the fibres in the muscle bundle shown in our diagram look different. They are, in fact, modified muscle fibres – cross-striated at their tapering ends only and encircled around their middles by nerve endings quite different from those handing on the motor commands to the normal load-bearing and load-lifting muscle fibres. These spiral endings are sensory and are also called primary endings by the physiologists to distinguish them from others on either side of them looking like a 'spray of flowers' when stained and inspected under the microscope – the secondary sensory endings of the physiologists. The modified muscle fibres bearing such sensory nerve endings usually lie together in groups and form

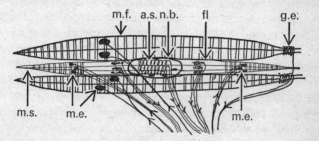

Figure 21. This is a sketch of a muscle spindle (m.s.) lying among four ordinary striated muscle fibres (m.f.). Only the ends of the three spindle fibres are striated. In the middle bulges the so-called nuclear bag (n.b.), harbouring the annulo-spiral or primary sensory endings (a.s.). Flower-spray or secondary sensory endings lie on either side of the nuclear bag (fl). The nerve connexions conduct, as shown by the arrow-heads, the motor impulses to the motor endings (m.e.) both on the ordinary and on the spindle muscle and sensory impulses from the sensory endings in the opposite direction towards the central nervous system. There are tendons with Golgi endings at one end of the ordinary muscle fibres (g.e.).

spindle-shaped 'inserts' distributed among the load-bearing bulk of the muscle fibres.

The muscle fibres are attached to the bones of the limb by sinews, and a close microscopic study of the connective tissue fibres making up these sinews or tendons shows that they, too, are provided with nerve endings, all of which are sensory. They are known as Golgi endings. Thus each one of the large nerve trunks 'innervating' a muscle contains a very considerable proportion of nerve fibres which conduct sensory information away from the muscle towards the central nervous system, besides the motor fibres carrying the central nervous command signals towards the ordinary muscle fibres.

The description of the analysis of the functioning of the muscle receptors fills volumes of physiological journals, and many of the fine points are still a matter of dispute or uncertainty. All the same, it is quite possible now to give a reasonably accurate account of how muscular activity is reflexly regulated, and to demonstrate the idea of an intricate mechanism of automatic control or automation, the likes of which would baffle the constructional engineer by its utter simplicity and reliability.

Let us assume first that the load on my arm muscles is suddenly increased, say by the server at the counter of a self-service canteen putting a few more potatoes on a plate which I hold out to her. The biceps muscle is being passively stretched and, if nothing is done about it, the plate will slant down and the food will fall off. I need not think or worry about it – automation will look after my food. The stretched muscle contains many muscle spindles – they become stretched with the rest of the muscle and this stimulates the nerve endings coiled around the spindle fibres. An increasing number of nerve impulses run up the sensory nerve and after they are relayed in the spinal cord on to motor command neurons, the load-bearing muscles are made to increase their tension by exactly the necessary amount sufficient to counteract the additional load of potatoes on plate and outstretched arm.

What if, under less pleasant circumstances the load put on to a limb were dangerously heavy – would the limb still be encouraged by this sort of reflex to hold it? The answer is no. There is a safety device built in to prevent overload, and this consists of the sensory nerves innervating the tendons by which the muscle is anchored to the bone. Before the muscle can be damaged or the tendons overstrained, signals from the tendon organs are sent to the command neurons in the spinal cord, and they, instead of making the muscle increase its ten-

sion in a vain and dangerous attempt to hold the overload,
bring about a relaxation of the muscles, and the limb gives in.
The load slides off and all is safe. The tendon organs are far
less sensitive than the muscle spindles and thus come into
action when the muscle is being overstretched.

So far we have considered reactions to passive loading.
Active movements or voluntary movements have also to be
controlled to prevent overshoot, as we saw when we considered the design of a robot. Let us assume a muscle is under a
certain amount of tension brought about by the weight of the
limb itself. Let this be my arm hanging down by my side. I
now 'will' the forearm to be moved up. Command signals are
sent from the motor centres in my brain to the spinal cord and
thence to the biceps muscle of my arm. The tension which
existed before the deliberate contraction of the muscle has
been signalled to the spinal cord by the muscle spindles tick-
ing over at a certain rate. Now the muscle obeys the command
and contracts. The muscle spindles, which don't share a
motor innervation with the load-bearing muscle fibres, will
not contract with them. They slacken, and their signalling
rate diminishes or stops after the muscle has shortened to a
certain extent – such a dying down of signals from the spindle
has the effect of stopping the further contraction and thus of
preventing the overshoot of the arm movement. The exact
point at which contraction is made to stop depends on the
initial length of the spindle fibres, and consequently on the
amount of slackening during muscular contraction. This
spindle fibre length can be set by the contraction of the
striated end-portions of the spindle fibre, which are under
separate command from small neurons in the spinal cord
lying side by side with the motor neurons which control the
load-bearing part of the muscle. The setting of the spindle
fibres can be influenced by command centres in the brain
prescribing the intended range of a limb movement.

Our story is becoming complicated. A further complication arises from the fact that for each muscle moving a limb one way, there is at least one other moving it in the opposite direction. The biceps (Figure 22) which flexes our arm is counteracted or antagonized by the triceps, which extends or straightens it. Sherrington worked out the remarkable coordination between such antagonistic pairs of flexor and

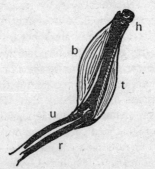

Figure 22. This shows the two chief muscles of the human upper arm. The biceps or flexor (b) acts as the antagonist to the triceps or extensor muscle (t). The muscles are attached to the humerus (h) and to the radius and ulna (r, u).

extensor muscles. They receive on every occasion exactly opposite commands from the command centre. When one is made to contract by proprioceptive reflex, its antagonist is made to relax simultaneously. All movements are smooth and are carried out within the safety limits of the load-bearing capacity of muscles and tendons.

The jerky movements of a spastic patient show how necessary this control mechanism is in such a simple activity as walking. The feedback of information from the muscles is defective in a spastic. One of the routine tests included in a general medical examination is designed to show whether the spinal reflex system is in order. This is the 'knee-jerk' test.

The physician asks the subject to sit with one knee over the other, the relaxed upper leg dangling down. He then reaches for a little metal mallet and deftly taps the tendon below the knee-cap. This imposes a short and smart stretch on the tendon and through it on the stretcher muscle of the leg. Its muscle spindles are stretched and the spinal command centre responds by making the stretcher muscle contract. The leg straightens with a jerk and the foot shoots forwards. If this reflex proved absent there is cause for a further, more thorough investigation of the spinal reflex system.

Automatic control mechanisms, especially when they are very critically set and highly sensitive, are liable to oscillate quite violently at times between correction, overcorrection, countercorrection, and so on. The engineer calls this hunting. A rather troublesome case of hunting in a domestic appliance occurs in a thermostatically controlled central heating plant. This heats up – overshoots – cools down too much – then overcompensates for this by overheating and so on. The effect is that the room oscillates between too hot and too cold, and never settles down at the desired temperature.

Automatic steering in cars can hunt dangerously unless a stabilizing mechanism is imposed upon it. Thus the proprioceptive spinal control mechanism of muscular movement is found to be subject to the stabilizing influence of higher brain centres. They utilize additional and overridingly important sensory information. Take the maintenance of an upright body posture. It is true the assessment of the distribution of pressure on the soles of the feet by pressure receptors in the skin or the spinal computing of the balance of stresses on the tendons and muscles of the leg, of the back and the neck by themselves can hold a body upright for a time. Correction and countercorrection can, however, easily produce hunting, and the body would begin to sway about the vertical. In daylight, a glance at the horizon or at a stable vertical feature can help to fix the orientation of the body and stabilize the proprioceptive control mechanism. In fact, visual control plays an important part in postural adjustment. This need not be conscious control by the highest centres in the cortex, and is in fact entrusted to reflex circuits in the cerebellum, a part of the brain concerned with the master control of coordination of posture and movement.

The ear labyrinth as an automatic pilot

But, one may ask, what happens in darkness or how does a blind person keep an upright posture? The answer is that – as usual in biological systems – there exists yet another safety factor in the shape of what may be called a sort of automatic pilot mechanism. It is found in our inner ear. Our inner ear (Figure 23) consists of two portions, the coiled-up cochlea and the so-called ear labyrinth. As we shall see in Chapter 7, the cochlea is the seat of sound receptors and the organ of pitch analysis. The ear labyrinth is the automatic pilot. It is fundamentally a fluid-filled bag subdivided into chambers. Three fluid-filled canals emerge from the main chamber. They each widen at one end into a roughly spherical chamber or ampulla. Each of the ampullae contains a sensory structure which together with the associated fluid-filled canal functions as what an engineer would call an accelerometer. This means the structure is sensitive to accelerated movement. The three canals lie in three different planes of space and are known as the semicircular canals of the inner ear.

The way in which they function is childishly simple. Imagine a circular basin filled with water. On the water surface float the usual specks of dust. You now begin to swivel the basin slowly, and you will see, when you look at the specks of dust, that they do not, for quite a while, join in the movement of the basin. Inertia makes them stay behind and they give evidence of a relative movement between the water and the wall of the basin. The same happens in a semicircular canal when we turn or tilt our head in the plane in which it lies. The fluid becomes displaced in a direction opposite to the head movement and therefore moves either towards the ampulla or away from it.

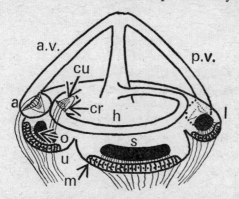

Figure 23. This is a diagrammatic representation of the ear labyrinth of a fish. Three semicircular canals, the anterior vertical (a.v.) the posterior vertical (p.v.) and the horizontal canal (h), widen each into an ampulla at one end (a). The ampullae contain crests of sensory hair cells (cr), the hair processes of which are ensheathed in a jelly-like cupula (cu). There are three otolith organs, the utriculus (u), the sacculus (s), and the lagena (l), each with a calcareous otolith (o) on its macula (m). The sensory cells in the maculae send their hair processes into the jelly in which the otolith is embedded. Our own labyrinth differs from the one shown here by having only two otolith organs (utriculus and sacculus) and by the sacculus giving rise to the coiled cochlea (see Figure 26).

Let us now look at the contents of an ampulla. It, too, is fluid-filled, and it communicates at the one end with the canal and at the other with one of the chambers of the labyrinth. In its centre there stands, freely balanced on a ridge in the floor, a tongue-shaped structure made of viscous jelly. It is known as the cupula and reaches from the ridge in the floor, the so-called crista, right up to the roof of the spherical ampulla. It has elastic springiness and returns to its original position whenever it has been bent in one or the other direc-

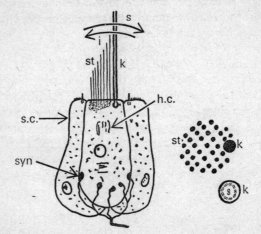

Figure 24. This is a hair cell (h.c.) from the ear labyrinth as seen under the electron-microscope. It is flanked by two supporting cells (s.c.). At the top is the compound bundle of hair processes, the stereocilia (st) and the single kinocilium (k) with its complex root. A more highly magnified cross-section through the hair bundle shows the position of the kinocilium, the 9 + 2 filamental structure of which is shown at a still greater magnification. Bending the hair bundle in the direction (s) stimulates the activity of the nerve processes synapsing with the base of the hair cell (syn). Bending in direction (i) inhibits their activity. The hair cells in the cochlea differ from those in the labyrinth by having the kinocilium represented by its root only. The stereocilia are present.

tion by a fluid movement in the canal. It behaves, in fact, like a spring-loaded pendulum. The crista is covered by a layer of cells of two types: sensory hair cells and supporting cells (Figure 24). We shall have a closer look at the sensory hair cells later on. As their name indicates, they are equipped with delicate hair processes, which protrude from the top of their cell bodies and extend far up into the jelly of the cupula in which they are embedded. At their base the cells are connected to sensory nerve endings which make intimate synaptic contact with the cell wall. In this way the hair cells mediate between the cupula pendulum and the ear nerve. When the cupula is passively pushed to one side or other, the delicate hair processes are bent and this sets up changes in the sensory cell that ultimately give rise to a coded signal in the sensory nerve. This conveys information about the degree and direction of bending of the sensory hairs. As the three semicircular canals lie in three planes of space approximately at right angles to each other – one horizontal and two vertical – they can sample turning movements of the head in any direction and, together, analyse it into its spatial components. The central nervous computing centre upon which the coded messages from the three canals converge can then accurately register the direction and extent of the head movements.

All this deals with speed and direction of movement. Postural control, too, is looked after by sense endings in the ear labyrinth. These lie in the main chamber. Again there are sensory hair cells assembled in patches or 'maculae' at the bottom of the chamber (e.g. utriculus). Their somewhat shorter hair processes are embedded in a jelly-like membrane, which is encrusted with crystals of lime. These form a so-called earstone or otolith. An otolith is specifically heavier than the surrounding fluid and tissues, and can be compared with the lead at the end of a plumbline, in so far as it tends to point vertically downwards, whatever the position of the floor of the labyrinth in space. Changes in position of the head in space will therefore make the heavy otolith push the jelly-like otolith membrane forwards or backwards, towards left or right, and bring about a corresponding bending of the sensory hairs. Again a flow of nerve impulses furnishes a signal 'informing' the central nervous computing centre of the direction and degree of deviation of the head from the vertical. We have thus in the labyrinth delicately poised dynamic and static receptors for the registration of turning movements and changes in posture.

It has been the author's good fortune to be able to contribute to the detailed analysis of these sensory mechanisms, and it may therefore be appropriate to choose them as an example to illustrate the way in which the sensory messages are coded and transmitted to the central nervous system. Let us choose as our specific example the horizontal semicircular canal of the left ear. It is obvious that this could not have been studied and experimentally analysed in a human ear. Fortunately, the inner ear of certain fish happens to have similar dimensions and an identical structure. Fortunately again, it was found that the organ of these cold-blooded animals remains functionally intact for hours after the death of the fish. This made it possible to analyse the nervous responses in a surviving ear of a fish that had been painlessly killed and disposed of. The fish in question was the thornback ray or skate that very frequently finds its way into the fish-and-chip shops under the name of 'rock turbot'. It is a so-called cartilaginous fish related to the sharks, but is flat and shaped like a kite. The advantageous thing about it is that its skull and skeleton are made up of soft translucent gristle instead of opaque hard bone, and that its tissues and organs are hardy and can survive without supply of oxygen in the absence of an intact blood circulation.

We look in on an electrophysiological experiment

The experiment takes place at a Marine Biological Laboratory. A ray of about 1 foot 9 inches wing span is selected from the sea-water tank and painlessly killed. The skull is then dissected away from the body, and the brain removed. We are thus left with a roughly square 'box' of gristle with two inner ears contained in those parts of the skull-case lying on either side of the now empty brain-cavity. After removal of the rather tough skin and of the eye, the gristle is carefully sliced away layer by layer until in the depth of the eye-socket the ampulla of the horizontal semicircular canal begins to shine through. From now on the removal of further gristle is a very delicate dissection, which aims at the exposure of the short stretch of nerve innervating the ampulla. When this has been achieved, a little slice of nerve is peeled off from below upwards and is inserted between the prongs of a silver-plated forceps which is fitted into an angled holder. This is fastened to the base-plate on which the preparation is securely mounted. A second silver wire is put in contact with the skull, and we are now ready to plug the lead from the two electrodes into a high-gain amplifier. This is a specially designed piece of radio equipment with amplification of about one million times. Such a high gain is necessary because the action potentials of about one-tenth of a volt (see Introduction, p. 18) are severely short-circuited by the moist tissues of the preparation and are therefore reduced to about a 1/50,000 of a volt. The amplifier is in turn connected to an oscillograph. This piece of equipment is comparable to a television set on the tube-face of which the image of a rapidly moving electronic beam is displaced. The beam moves from side to side and when an amplified action impulse of a potential is imposed upon the beam it is deflected upwards for the very short duration of the impulse (1/1,000 of a second). A blip is seen on the horizontal trace on the screen. This can be photographed by a film camera and a series of such blips are shown in Figure 25. At the same time we can make the blips audible in a loudspeaker and a rapid sequence of impulses sounds like a muffled burst of machine-gun fire.

If we are lucky we may now, in fact, hear such a sequence of impulses intercepted from one of the fibres of the ampullary nerve, which lies closest to the metal of the pick-up electrode.

This is the activity from a single sensory cell in the crista of the horizontal canal, and as our preparation is not being moved about at the moment, we call this the resting discharge. We find that, at rest, our single sensory cell fires off about 3 impulses per second.

We now mount the preparation carefully on a turn-table so that the horizontal canal in the isolated skull lies in a horizontal plane. The exciting moment of testing for the organ's

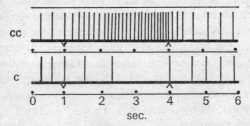

Figure 25. This is an oscillographic recording from the left horizontal semicircular canal of the thornback ray, as obtained in the experiment described in the text. Note the increase of discharge rate on counterclockwise (cc) and its decrease and complete abolition on clockwise (c) rotation. The arrows pointing upwards denote the start and those pointing downwards the end of rotation.

response to turning has come. Very gently we set the turn-table in motion. Remembering that we are working on the left ear we turn the table towards the left (counterclockwise). Immediately, during the gentle acceleration of the turn-table from rest, the frequency of the impulse discharge begins to rise. An acceleration of as little as $10°/sec.^2$ may double the discharge frequency during the first second. After 3 seconds our turn-table has reached a speed of $30°/second$ and the preparation may now discharge at a rate of 12 impulses per second. All this has been recorded on film. We now let the table go on without further acceleration. The friction in the table slows it down, and immediately the discharge frequency of the sensory cell begins to fall and returns to its resting rate when the table has come to a standstill. We conclude that the change in the discharge rate must have been due to a deflection of the cupula and the bending of the hair processes of our sensory cell away from the canal; in fact, in a direction opposite to that of the turn-table movement.

The effect, then, of turning the left canal to the left was an increase in excitation in the sensory cells of its ampulla. We now just as gently begin to turn the turn-table to the right (clockwise) and immediately the rate of discharge from the sensory cell falls and is silenced completely by the time the turn-table reaches the speed of 30°/second. As the turn-table is now allowed to slow down the discharge reappears and finally reaches the resting level of 3 impulses per second. We assume that during the right turn the cupula was deflected towards the canal, i.e. again in a direction opposite to that of the rotation of the turn-table.

It can be shown in this way that the bending of the hair processes of the sensory cells in the ampulla of a semicircular canal produces an increase in the number of signals/second, and bending in the opposite direction inhibits the electrical activity of the cell which leads to a decrease in firing rate or even a complete silencing of the cell. All these responses can thus be studied quantitatively, and we can gain an understanding of the reactions of single sensory cells under conditions of natural stimulation. And all this can be studied in the surviving sense organ of a dead fish! Unfortunately we have to leave the laboratory now, but the close study of one specific experiment should bring us nearer to an understanding of the fundamental aspects of how sensory information is coded during transmission from sense organ to central nervous system.

The ultrastructure of the sensory cell

Let us now have a closer look at a sensory cell in the crista of a semicircular canal. For this exercise we shall find the magnification of even the most powerful light-microscope insufficient. The electron-microscope with its useful magnification of up to half a million times is the proper instrument for this purpose. It reveals immediately (Figure 24) that the hair process from our sensory cell is a complex structure consisting of about fifty separate filaments or cilia. One of these is different from the rest. In fact, it resembles the structure of a flagellum or cilium (see Chapter 2). At its base it has a root exactly as we would find it in a cilium on a ciliate protozoan or on the ciliated cells covering the gill of a shell-fish where the cilia are organs of movement, moving the organism or moving along fluids and particles within an organism.

Here in the ear these hairs cannot move actively. They are ensheathed in the jelly of the cupula. But when the cupula is being deflected they are passively bent, and it is thought that this brings about an electric change near their root. In a way as yet unknown this electric change is transferred to the nerve endings which embrace the lower end of the sensory cell and make close synaptic contact with it. Only one of the hair processes of each cell is a cilium of this kind, and is called kinocilium. It is recognizable under the electron-microscope by the presence of nine outer and two inner longitudinal filaments inside it. The other hair processes are fairly structureless inside and look solid in cross-section. They are called stereocilia and it may be assumed that their united springiness helps in providing the elastic force which brings the cupula back to its resting position after it has been bent this way or that by the inertia in the canal fluid. The position of the kinocilium within the hair bundle is fixed and suggestive of its function. In the cells of the ampulla of a semicircular canal it stands in a niche on one side of the bundle of the stereocilia. And this is the side towards which the hair bundle is bent when the cells are made to fire faster. This suggests a close connexion between the arrangement of hairs and excitation or inhibition of the sensory hair cells and the nerves innervating them.

We have thus reached a point where we can attempt to link the minute structural details of the sensory cells with their behaviour, when they are tested singly by the interception of the nervous message passing along the nerve fibre connecting them with the central nervous system. This is as far as we want to go here, and, it may be confessed, this is as far as we can go at present, because we have truly reached the frontier of knowledge in this field.

To return now to matters on a larger scale, to our automatic pilot. Its proper functioning in monitoring and controlling active and passive movements of head and body depends on the smooth collaboration of thousands of sensory cells deployed in an orderly arrangement and on the coding of nerve impulses, as well as on the transit of frequency-coded nerve impulses along bundles of nerve fibres to the central nervous control station. There the coded information is decoded and converted into the appropriate commands for the high-level control of posture and movement, and especially for the stabilization of the automatic lower-level processes entrusted to the kinesthetic and proprioceptive sense endings in the skin and joints and in muscles and tendons. A thorough knowledge of how this 'automatic pilot' functions has always been of great clinical importance in the diagnosis of the cause of disturbed balance and nausea in patients with inner-ear disease or brain lesions. Space travel, in which the ear labyrinth is exposed to entirely new conditions such as weightlessness or increased gravitational pull during blast off or re-entry, is now posing a number of difficult new problems, such as the possibility of disorientation and space sickness in astronauts. A great deal of research is, therefore, going on at present in which the reactions of the ear labyrinth to this type of 'unnatural' stimulation are being investigated.

The importance of visual information in the final control of posture and movement has been pointed out. The visual control of posture and movement is greatly aided by an automatic adjustment of the position of the eye in the head. This is brought about by a system of static and dynamic reflexes of the eye muscles to change of position (see Figure 7). When I move my head, the information from the semi-circular canals and from the utriculi is relayed to the central nervous station dealing with the contraction and relaxation of two of the six muscles inserting on the eyeball. These muscles are arranged in pairs. There is an upper and lower, and an inner and outer straight muscle. These lift or lower the gaze and turn the eye from side to side respectively. Two oblique muscles roll the eye in orbit either clockwise or counterclockwise. Bending the head forward makes the upper straight muscle contract and the lower straight one relax. The result is that my gaze is automatically directed upwards so that the image of my surroundings stays roughly on the same place on the retina. The opposite happens on raising the head. Turning the head from side to side produces automatic counter-movements of the eyes brought about by the inner and outer straight muscles. Sideways tilting of the head is compensated for by rolling counter-movements of the eyes due to the contraction of the pairs of oblique eye muscles. Thus we retain during movement as steady as possible a picture of our environment.

In voluntary changes in posture and in the voluntary movement involved in deliberate activity, visual orientation can of course be a conscious process, interfering with and overriding the automatic mechanisms.

7

MECHANORECEPTORS III

Hearing

IT is sometimes said that 'things are quite simple until a scientist comes along and complicates them', or that the scientist is occupied in converting common sense into uncommon sense. The standard example for this is the revelation by Copernicus and Galileo that, contrary to commonsense experience, the sun stands still and does not move from East to West in a daily race across the firmament.

We all know what we mean by 'hearing' and by 'sound', and yet both terms are being hotly debated whenever scientists attempt to define them rigorously. What is sound? Sound is what we can hear. What is hearing? The perception of sound. These circular definitions are very reminiscent of what the uninitiated may find in a dictionary when he wants to inform himself about the game of Badminton. Badminton, it says, is a game played with a shuttlecock and a battledore (see shuttlecock and battledore). When looking up these strange terms one is informed that they are implements used in a game known as Badminton, and this adds considerably to enlightenment. Fortunately, not all dictionaries are as bleak as this. We, too, must try to get out of the circularity in the definition of hearing by divesting the concept of sound of its immediate psychological 'overtones'.

Physically, we may say that sound is a mechanical disturbance propagated in matter by means of longitudinal waves of compression and decompression. But in order to qualify as sound waves and not as seismic earthquake waves or as supersonic waves, they must lie within a limited range of frequencies. Limited by what? Why, of course, by being audible to at least some animal organism. And here we are back to our circularity. Not in its extremest form though, since we don't confine sound reception to *human* hearing. But, you may well ask, how do we know whether a given animal can hear? What if such an animal *feels* the sound waves with its organs of touch, as we can feel the sound of a mighty organ with our fingertips on the church pew? Is this hearing? It has been suggested that the term hearing should in fact be confined to such cases where the sense organ which is stimulated by such a wave of compression and decompression resembles the human ear. How close has this resemblance to be? Insects have so-called tympanal organs in their bellies or even in their legs, and these organs can be shown to transduce airborne 'sound' waves into electrical nerve impulses, which form the stimulus for the insect's behavioural responses to the 'sound'. Are we entitled to say insects can hear? I think the answer is yes – some people have thought otherwise.

For a long time it was assumed by physiologists that fish are deaf, because their inner ears, the sense organs for the maintenance of balance found in their head, correspond only to the labyrinths of the human inner ear and are devoid of a cochlea. The cochlea is appended to the ear labyrinth in the higher backboned animals and is especially well developed in birds and mammals. It has long been recognized as the seat of human hearing, and its total absence in fishes led to the assumption that fish are deaf, an assumption that has always had a false 'ring' to the ear of fishermen, gamekeepers, and naturalists. As we shall see, most fish do in fact hear pretty well. At the other extreme, it has been suggested that we should use the term hearing whenever an animal organism reacts to 'sound' waves irrespective of frequency and of the nature of the receptor organ by being able to locate their source of origin; that is to say, by being able to ascertain the direction of their pathway. This would be a useful definition of hearing, if it was not for the fact that fish, with their very sensitive sound perception and quite remarkable power of discrimination for pitch within a certain range, are capable only of very poor or no directional localization of the sound source.

It is clear, therefore, that we have to be content with talking about sound and hearing without trying to define these terms too rigorously. Thus the terms subsonic and ultrasonic will have to be related entirely to the receptive range of the human ear. How, then, does the human sound spectrum fit into the general spectrum of mechanical as opposed to electromagnetic waves?

The longest electromagnetic waves used for broadcasting are measured in kilometres (thousands of yards) and their frequency may be as 'low' as 100,000 cycles per second. Of course, their speed of propagation is very high – 186,000 miles per second. 'Sound' waves travel much more slowly. In air their speed of propagation is only about 1,100 feet per second. Through water and through solids sound passes much faster depending on the density of the medium. We use, therefore, frequencies rather than wavelengths as units of measurement. The note of middle C on the piano has a frequency of 256 cycles per second, and average human hearing ranges from roughly 16 to 20,000 cycles. This means it covers about eleven octaves, the frequency of a note being twice that of a note of the same name an octave below it. If we divided the visible electromagnetic spectrum similarly into octaves, our vision would be found to range barely over one octave (350–700 mμ) of the spectrum, the shortest visible wavelength having about twice the frequency of the longest. The range of the sound spectrum given above relates to young people only. From early middle age onwards it shortens gradually at the higher frequency end, and by the age of fifty some of us can no longer hear notes above 10,000 cycles. Cats hear up to 50,000, and bats up to 120,000 cycles.

At the low-frequency end we may in fact not really hear an organ note of 16 cycles. What we hear may be upper harmonics such as 32 cycles and others produced by this very long pipe tuned to produce a fundamental note of 16 cycles. If we use a piece of apparatus which produces single-frequency notes without harmonics, we find that below 16 cycles the sound is not that of a single sustained tone, but that of say ten discrete sound pulses, each of which is just a throb of noise without sound 'colour'.

The use of the word sound 'colour' brings to mind the analogy between colour and pitch. As we see a spectrum of colours, so we hear a spectrum of sounds of different pitch. One difference is noteworthy. Whereas a number of colours offered to the eye simultaneously and in the same area of visible space always blend to result in a new hue (see Chapter 3), a chord of three or more notes of different pitch offered simultaneously does not fuse and the notes remain discrete. Perhaps the nearest approach to blending is the smooth sound of two simultaneously sounded notes an octave apart.

We are not going to get immersed in mathematical accoustics, harmony, and counterpoint, just as we could not, when dealing with vision, get enthusiastic over geometrical optics. What we want to find out is how we hear. As always, we shall also inquire into the hearing powers of our fellow animals within the rather vague boundaries of definition of hearing.

To get better acquainted with the design and way of functioning of the human ear, we might usefully listen in at lectures on the subject given to a class of young students of physiology. The lantern slides referred to by the lecturer correspond to the illustrations in the text. We may expect these lectures to be followed by questions and discussion which, if we are lucky, will clear up doubtful points and misunderstandings, as well as provide us with an explanation of some of the rather strange technical terms.

We attend a lecture on the function of the ear

In this lecture we are going to acquaint ourselves with the general lay-out of the human ear and, faithful to the principle that form can only be properly understood when its functional

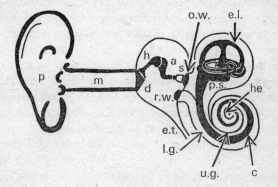

Figure 26. This is a diagrammatic sketch of the human outer, middle, and inner ear. The pinna (p) leads into the meatus (m). The drum (d) separates the outer from the middle ear. The three ossicles, hammer (h), anvil (a), and stirrup (s), lead to the oval window (o.w.). The middle-ear cavity is connected with the cavity of the mouth by the Eustachian tube (e.t.). In the inner-ear cavity lies the fluid-filled ear labyrinth (e.l.) with its appendage, the coiled cochlea (c). This is coiled up in a helical space filled with perilymph (p.s.). This space is divided by the cochlear duct into an upper and a lower gallery (u.g., l.g.) which communicate with one another through the helicotrema (he) at the tip of the cochlear duct. The lower gallery is separated from the middle-ear cavity by a membrane covering the round window (r.w.). The cochlear duct, like the ear labyrinth, is filled with endolymph (black).

importance is taken into consideration, we shall inquire into the mode of functioning of the component parts of this very complex organ. Slide 1 [Figure 26] is a general plan of the ear. The shape of the outer ear or pinna, of course, varies enormously in different people and different races. There are big and small ears, ears with free and grown-on lobes, long ears and floppy ears. Some lie close to the skull, others stand away a mile. I was very impressed when, during a stay in Africa, I asked an African what they thought to be particularly strange in the appearance of Europeans. He mentioned our big ugly ears, before commenting on our rosy-pink, white, or 'green' complexion. This made me look at the ears of Africans, and I found that almost without exception they are small and extremely well-shaped.

What do the shape and especially the various folds and convolutions mean functionally? One might be inclined to think that the pinna's function is to collect sound waves like a concave mirror collects light. A gadget which is meant to collect waves must be considerably larger than the waves. Our searchlight mirrors are exactly this. The wavelengths they have to deal with are measured in mμ and the mirrors measure several feet across. The sound waves coming towards us from all sides, however, have wavelengths measured in many inches, feet, or even yards, whereas the diameter of the pinna and especially of the inner conch is not much more than 1 inch. The sound is therefore scattered rather than collected and focused.

Some of the scattered sound reaches the corridor or meatus of the ear. This, together with the conch, acts like the sound-box of a violin by resonating with a range of those scattered sound waves. The outer ears of many of our fellow mammals are of course much bigger and often movable, so that the animal can scan over quite a considerable angle by turning its pinnae rather than its head. This helps it to localize the origin of the sound. The ear of the horse is moved about by no fewer than seventeen different muscles. We have only nine, and they are not up to much. Only few of us can wag our ears rather ineffectually, as I can. [Laughter in the audience.] If we want to locate a source of sound we have to turn our head, and this may be fateful, if danger approaches from several directions at once, including from straight ahead. What function the various convolutions of the pinna have is obscure. You see, the pinna of apes and monkeys is much less sculptured, and yet one would have thought that in the wild any advantage connected with such folds would have led to their preservation or even increased development. Should it have something to do with the more highly complex wave pattern used in human communication by speech? I have to leave this question open.

Let us now go into the ear channel or meatus. It is about an inch long and its surface is lubricated with a layer of ear wax. When we insert a finger into it we find it warm and cosy in there. The entry into it carries a fringe of hair. All these are protective devices. The hairs are a dust curtain and shield the entrance to a certain extent against intruders, such as small insects. If they get beyond the hair fringe, they will find further progress a sticky affair and may be caught as it were on fly-paper. So you see the proverbial flea in the ear hasn't a very gay time! It is quite on the cards that it will never reach the delicate ear-drum or tympanic membrane at the other end of the corridor. Delicate is the word. The drum is only about 1/3,000 of an inch thick and translucent. Children who suffer a lot from ear-ache have to have their drums punctured by a doctor now and again. Normally, such a puncture heals fairly quickly.

The warmth in the meatus establishes fairly constant temperature conditions near the drum and in the middle and inner ear. This is necessary because the whole ear mechanism is highly sensitive to temperature change. When we dealt with that part of the inner ear which is concerned with balance, you will remember that the function of the semicircular canals of the fluid-filled labyrinth is based on delicate movements of this fluid. Such movement could occur if the temperature of the system were allowed to fluctuate violently. In fact, in a set of clinical tests in patients whose sense of balance is upset by inner-ear disease, water of slightly higher or lower than body temperature is flushed into and out of the meatus in order to set the mechanism of the semicircular canals in motion in a stationary patient. Disagreeably these tests can produce vertigo and nausea and they are rather disliked by sensitive patients. Such fits of vertigo would be produced if sudden cold blasts of air were to reach the drum or, worse still, if cold water were to get into the middle ear through a perforated drum during swimming or diving. This is why it is advisable for swimmers to plug the meatus if there is a suspicion of a burst drum. Of course, the mechanism of hearing itself depends on such a delicate interplay of mechanical forces that it, too, must be sheltered by constant temperature conditions.

Let us take advantage, however, of such an opening in the drum, and peep through it into the cavity of the middle ear known as the tympanum. This is a dome-shaped space which is spanned by a chain of three articulated bones with the picturesque names of hammer, anvil, and stirrup. The hammer is connected to the ear-drum, and the stirrup to an equally thin membrane stretched across the so-called oval window or *fenestra ovalis* at the far end of the middle-ear cavity. The anvil forms the connecting link of this chain of bones, which is not straight but forms an upward curved arch, the members of which are also angled in a horizontal plane.

Before we go on to deal with the function of this delicately articulated bony bridge between drum and oval window, it may be appropriate to remind the zoologists among you of the rather strange history of these three little bones. I am sure you have learnt in your course on comparative anatomy and evolution that these bones are thought to be derived by a long series of changes in shape and by shifts in position from the jaw skeleton of fish. They form there the joint by which the jaw is suspended from the skull. But this is only by the way. Let us return to function.

The middle-ear cavity is filled with air, but it is not entirely closed. From the bottom of it a thin canal, the so-called Eustachian tube, leads to the back of the mouth cavity. This drains fluid from the middle ear, whose walls are made up of moist tissue. The Eustachian tube also serves in pressure equalization. It is in fact the vent which you open more widely when you swallow hard to take pressure 'off your ears' during the rapid ascent or descent of the plane, when the air hostess makes her round, offering sweeties or chewing gum to her flock of passengers.

Unfortunately, it is through this mucus-filled Eustachian tube that an infective cold in nose or throat can reach the middle ear to cause the already mentioned ear-ache, which is due to a condition called otitis media. In this the middle-ear cavity can become filled up with pus, completely enveloping and gumming up the ear ossicles and making you temporarily deaf in the affected ear. This gives us straight away a hint about the function of the ear ossicles. They have to do with the conduction of sound waves from the drum to the oval window. The alternating waves of compression and decompression of the air move the delicate sheet of the drum tissue in and out. The drum in man has the shape of an inward-pointing cone which resembles, but for its size, the diaphragm of the loudspeaker in our radio or television set.

The ear-drum is under tension, and this is adjustable in a manner I shall describe in a moment. The bridge of three ossicles is articulated by joints between them. These joints can be stiffened by the action of two tiny muscles. The first acts on the hammer and is called tensor tympany, because its contraction increases the tensioning of the drum as well as the rigidity of the bridge. The second muscle, which is, by the way, the smallest muscle in our body, is called the stapedius muscle and acts on the stirrup. When it contracts the anvil–stirrup joint stiffens. The contractions of these muscles are normally not under the control of the will, but occur automatically as a reflex in response to sound. Details of their function have been the subject of quite a lot of dispute in the light of conflicting evidence. However, I don't think we go far wrong if we assume that a stiffening of the bony bridge is a protective device making transmission of sound less effective and in this way protecting the drum and the inner ear from damage from high-intensity sound. The little bones may, therefore, act as an automatic volume control.

The interesting fact is that the muscular adjustment counteracts the basic function of the bony bridge as an efficient transmitter of sound waves from drum to inner ear. When sound waves move in air they meet with very little resistance. Each wave is a to-and-fro movement traversing relatively considerable distances, depending on the wavelength. When the sound waves come up against the drum, they have to push it in and out and with it the long stalk of the hammer which is attached to the drum. The bridge formed by the three bones leads to the oval window, beyond which lies the fluid-filled inner ear. The membrane covering the oval window is much smaller and stiffer than the ear-drum and any movement of it inwards brought about by a rocking movement of the stirrup meets with the inert resistance of the inner-ear fluid. Our ear ossicles transform a relatively weak force acting on the drum into a force many times as strong acting on the oval window. We have here what the engineer would call a matching device for the matching of air-borne to fluid-borne power transmission. The whole process can be likened to what happens in a hydraulic press or a hydraulic jack by means of which a man operating a long pump handle can lift a heavy lorry from the ground. His arm, which we may liken to the ear-drum, moves a long way for a little lift (movement of the oval window). In the end he has not done any less work, but all the way through his strength is never overtaxed. You see now how efficient the drum and ossicles are in transmitting sound and how in doing so their dimensions guarantee that the inner-ear fluid is not made to swill about too much. As you will presently hear, the structures of the inner ear are incredibly delicate and small, and, on the other hand, very dense and rigid. Small, but relatively powerful, movements are therefore what is needed for their stimulation. The more efficient the hydraulic device, however, the greater is the danger of destructive overstimulation; hence the automatic volume control by the muscular reflex contraction of the middle-ear muscles.

We have now arrived at the oval window. This separates the tympanal cavity from the fluid-filled spaces of the inner ear containing the ear-labyrinth and its appendage the cochlea. When sound waves arrive at the oval window the rocking motion of the stirrup pushes it in and out. The fluid of the inner ear surrounding the ear labyrinth and the cochlea is known as endolymph. Through it the sound waves move along. They are prevented from upsetting the receptors of the labyrinth by being absorbed there in a padding of spongy connective tissue. This forms, as it were, a layer of 'cotton wool' surrounding the semicircular canals and the utriculus.

The next slide [Figure 27] shows how the waves may be imagined to travel into the perilymph-filled space surrounding the cochlea. This is subdivided into a gallery that runs above the cochlear duct from base to tip. At the tip there is an opening, the helicotrema, through which this upper gallery communicates with a lower one. This runs below the cochlear duct from tip to base and ends there at yet another window. This is known as the round window and, like the oval window, is covered by an elastic membrane. When the pressure waves are propagated through the perilymph they run up the upper and back along the lower gallery and finally reach the round

window. This can be made to bulge out into the tympanal
cavity. When the oval window bulges in, the round one is
pushed out and vice versa. The wave of pressure conducted
via the ear ossicles to the oval window and thence through
the perilymph of the two galleries to the round window re-

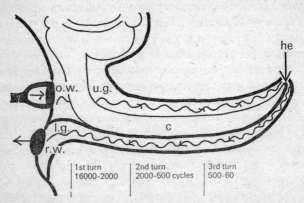

Figure 27. This is a highly diagrammatic plan of the cochlear duct of
the ear (c). The pathway of the sound waves can be followed from the
oval window (o.w.) along the upper gallery (u.g.) and back along the
lower gallery (l.g.) to the round window (r.w.). The sound waves can,
however, take short cuts across the cochlear duct at various distances
from the base, instead of travelling all the way via the helicotrema
(he). The whole structure is of course relatively much longer and
coiled up in the form of a helical staircase.

turns thus to the air space of the tympanal cavity, where
it can find an outlet through the Eustachian tube and the mouth
back full circle to the atmospheric air where it came from.

This closed circuit guarantees a free passage of the sound
waves past the cochlear duct. The cochlear duct forms the
middle gallery. It is filled with endolymph like the labyrinth of
which it is an outgrowth. It harbours the sensory hair cells and
nerve endings responsible for sound perception and analysis of
pitch. The three galleries are in mammals accommodated in

the otic bone of the skull and are coiled up into a three-decker spiral staircase. In most mammals, including ourselves, there are three turns of this spiral coil; in some there are fewer, in some four. You will hear in the next lecture how the sensory cells in the cochlear duct are stimulated and, especially, how complex sounds are sorted out there so as to convey to the central nervous system correct information about the frequency, composition, and intensity of orderly sound and disorderly noise.

I think the time has come for me to interrupt my talk. Before I resume I shall be pleased as usual to answer questions.

The lecturer answers questions

STUDENT A: Elephants have very large ear-flaps. Do you think these might be big enough to focus sound?

LECTURER: So far as pure dimensions are concerned they might be. But look at their shape. It is not exactly that of a smooth parabolic mirror is it? Certainly they can catch a bigger bundle of sound waves, so to speak, and therefore their directional discrimination has a longer range, as befits such large animals. Yet look at the nimble ears of giraffes. They do just as well. Elephants' ear-flaps, as you call them, have an interesting additional function. They act as thermoregulators or simply as radiators for the cooling of the blood. When the elephants flap them about, which they do rhythmically at a frequency increasing with increasing heat, quite a considerable volume of blood circulating through the pinnae gets cooled. A dog would hang its moist tongue out for the same purpose.

STUDENT A: Why haven't giraffes such thermo-regulators?

LECTURER: The biologically sound answer is: they haven't because they aren't elephants. And think of it. Giraffes would look a sight. They couldn't live up to this!

STUDENT B: I didn't quite understand the difference between focusing sound waves and scattering them. If they are scattered, isn't their wavelength changed? If so, we could never hear the proper pitch of a musical note.

LECTURER: What we go by physiologically is not the wavelength only but the frequency, and this is not altered by scattering. Even if we get only little bits of wave we get such little bits the same number of times a second. Therefore scattering may affect the total energy collected by the ear and may select some frequencies in favour of others, but it does not alter the pitch.

STUDENT C: As we cannot move our ear-flaps, are we able to distinguish direction equally well all round?

LECTURER: No, we are not. Under certain circumstances we aren't quite sure whether a noise reaches us from straight in front or from behind. This is due to the fact that such sound reaches both ears at the same time, and, as we shall explain later in greater detail, in directional hearing we compute the time difference in the stimulation of our two ears. Animals with movable pinnae are of course better off. They, too, have some difficulty in locating sound coming from above. Try to whistle to your dog from an upstairs window and you will see that he doesn't seem to know where the sound comes from. In this connexion it is interesting that owls have asymmetrically placed ears – one higher up on the head than the other. That means that they are able to locate sound quite well in the vertical plane as well as in the horizontal – a useful asset to a bird that catches flying insects on the wing and has to locate the rustling of a mouse on the ground below.

STUDENT A: The middle-ear cavity and the duct are very small spaces. How can they resonate in the way you said without making a mess of the incoming sound?

LECTURER: These cavities and other structures, like the drum and the ossicles of the middle ear, do in fact make a mess of the sound, as you put it. They introduce what is called harmonic distortion by giving preference to certain harmonics. I said I am not going to deal with physical acoustics, and I don't know whether you understand what I mean by harmonics. If a note is sounded – say the middle C on the piano – this contains other frequencies as well, such as, for instance, the C above. This harmonic content may in fact be unduly exaggerated by harmonic distortion in our ears. A referee's whistle contains two notes of about 1,000 and 1,250 cycles. But what we hear most strikingly is the difference tone of 250 cycles. Whether the world is really how it appears to us is an old philosophical problem which we shall have to deal with at some length at a later occasion.

STUDENT D: As we had no opportunity to dissect an ear, I wonder whether you could give us an idea of the various dimensions; for instance, of the size of the drum or of the ossicles or for that matter of the cochlea?

LECTURER: You are lucky that I have notes about this in front of me. I don't carry such numerical data in my head, nor do I burden my lectures with them, except when they are necessary to the understanding of a function. One can look this sort of information up in books. However, here goes: the drum has an area of about 90 mm.^{2} I don't think I can give you the exact measurements of the ear ossicles, but the important one is that the foot-plate of the stirrup has an area of about 3 mm.^{2} only. So you see the reduction in transmitting area between the air in the meatus and the perilymph in the inner ear at the oval window could be a thirtyfold one. This is functionally important, when you remember what I said about the comparison between middle ear and a hydraulic jack. The round window has an area of 2 mm.^{2}, which makes it roughly equal with the oval one. The total length of the human cochlea is only about 30 mm., i.e. about an inch and a fifth. If you consider this coiled up into three turns you see that the whole inner hearing organ is surprisingly minute. The helicotrema, the little communicating passage between the upper and the lower gallery opposite the tip of the cochlear duct, has an area of 0·25 mm.^{2}.

STUDENT B: What is otosclerosis?

LECTURER: This is a condition in which the connexion of the base of the stirrup with the oval window becomes hardened and stiff. This results in loss of hearing that can amount to a factor of up to a million times at all frequencies. This is very severe considering that our sensitivity range extends from a tone just barely audible to one at 10,000 million times the strength or volume. Ear surgeons have developed an operating technique in which they loosen this hardened connexion between stirrup and oval window. This can be quite successful in many cases in restoring a considerable proportion of the hearing loss.

STUDENT A: Should ear wax be removed or should we leave our ears alone?

LECTURER: A hardened plug of ear wax can accumulate under certain circumstances, and this leads to hearing loss. A doctor can remove it by careful syringing. In view of what I said about the possible effects of temperature change in the ear this should be done by a doctor. Generally speaking, ear wax, if continuously removed by a too thorough-going attention to the ear during the daily wash, will only be renewed the faster. On the other hand, a lot of it covering the walls of the cavity does not look very attractive, does it? So a happy medium of attention is the best policy.

STUDENT B: I wonder whether it really helps a lot to open one's mouth when one expects a very big bang? I should have thought this might make matters worse by allowing the round window to bulge instead of shutting it off from the outer air by keeping the mouth tightly closed.

LECTURER: All gunners learn to open their mouths as well as to cover their ears. When the mouth is open the sound pressure will act almost simultaneously on drum and round window, pushing them in opposite directions. This is better still than your suggested remedy. None of these precautions are always effective, and loud bangs can result in severe damage. We shall presently hear more about such damage in connexion with structures of the inner ear.

STUDENT E: There are quite a number of vertebrate animals without pinnae. Can they localize sound?

LECTURER: Yes, there are even *mammals* without pinnae. Do you know which?

STUDENT E: Whales, I guess.

LECTURER: Yes, whales and other cetaceans like dolphins have no pinnae. They would be useless because their density being not much different from that of water they cannot scatter water-borne sound waves efficiently. They would also get in the way of streamlining. And yet among all aquatic animals, whales and dolphins are the only ones with good directional hearing. They rely for this entirely on the distance between their two ears, together with the remarkable fact that their inner ears are slung freely from the skull so that they can be stimulated independently of each other and of the rest of the skull tissues. This, together with large air spaces around the inner ear, makes possible the accurate registration of time-differences in the arrival of sound waves and the computing from this of sound direction. By the way, in whales the meatus is very thin or completely solid and in dolphins the outer-ear opening is minute (0·5 mm. across). Nevertheless, even the solid 'meatus' is said to play a part in sound transmission in a way that I haven't time to describe. They all have a middle ear with drum and ossicles. These, too, show very interesting modifications in shape and dimensions for hearing under water. There are also some modifications to the inner-ear structures which are associated with the fact that whales and dolphins can hear in the 'ultrasonic' range.

But to return to your question, which concerned all vertebrates. Frogs, reptiles, and birds are without ear-flaps. In frogs and most reptiles the drum can be seen on the outside of the skull, but it is missing in newts and some toads. Snakes have no ear-drums, and hearing depends entirely on the reception of solid-bone vibrations through the ground. They certainly don't hear [the tune of the snake charmer, but follow his movements by eye.

STUDENT D: Are there insects that go for our ears? I am thinking of earwigs.

LECTURER: There is a lot of lore about them. I don't think any of them aim specifically at ears, but if you fall asleep in the open with your ear near the ground, you can't blame them if they occasionally find their way into the meatus and enjoy its sheltered cosiness. Pardon this unscientific assumption of enjoyment in an insect, but you know what I mean. Having come down to folk-lore we had better resume the scientific story of the ear and inquire about what goes on in the cochlea.

The lecture continues

We had arrived at the oval window. There we found the footplate of the stirrup rocking to and fro in the rhythm of the sound waves. The movement of the membrane covering the window transmits the sound waves to the perilymph of the upper and lower gallery. As they travel past the cochlear duct which forms the middle gallery, part of their energy is transferred to its walls and through them to the endolymph and all the structures contained in it. The upper wall or Reissner's membrane is a very thin sheet of tissue very delicately pliable.

Not so the lower wall or floor of the cochlear duct. Its texture can be compared with that of a reed carpet in which the warp is made of relatively stiff fibres short at the base and increasingly longer as we go up the coiled duct towards its tip. The woof interconnecting these fibres, of which there are about 4,000 in a human cochlea, mats them together into a floor

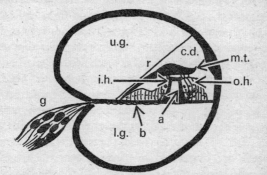

Figure 28. This is a cross-section through the cochlea. The cochlear duct (c.d.) occupies the middle and is separated from the upper gallery (u.g.) by Reissner's membrane (r), and from the lower gallery (l.g.) by the basilar membrane (b). On the basilar membrane rests one of the 4,000 arches of Corti (a). One inner hair cell (i.h.) and three outer ones (o.h.) are shown with their hair processes touching the membrana tectoria (m.t.). The nerve fibres from the hair cells run towards the inner aspect, where their cell bodies are seen to form the first-order ganglion of the acoustic nerve (g).

carpet. This has elastic springiness thanks to the elastic fibres of the warp, which are suspended between the inner and outer attachments to the bony support of the cochlea. It was at one time thought that these fibres are under quite considerable tension, but this has not been confirmed by more recent investigations.

The floor of the cochlear duct is known as the membrana basilaris or basilar membrane. In cross-section the cochlear duct is triangular. Next slide, please [Figure 28]. Its roof, Reissner's membrane, is suspended on a slope from the inner edge of the basilar membrane upwards. The outer wall of the cochlear duct is formed by glandular tissue which is thought to secrete the endolymph fluid. The basilar membrane carries a tunnel-shaped affair, the tunnel of Corti. This is made up of a series of about 4,000 arched structures, the 'arches of Corti', which form the support of one inner and three or four outer rows of sensory hair cells. The hair cells are very similar to those found in the ear labyrinth. From their tops emerge bundles of hair processes. These reach up to a jelly-like cover, the membrana tectoria. The tectorial membrane is fixed to the inner bony shaft of the cochlear spiral, but ends freely some distance beyond the three parallel rows of outer hair cells. The upper ends of the hair processes of the hair cells appear to just touch the lower surface of the tectorial membrane. The hair cells are innervated by nerve fibres which enter the cochlear duct from the inside of the coil. The cell bodies of the sensory neurons, from which these fibres spring, lie in a strip of tissue which accompanies the inner aspect of the cochlear duct, as it winds spirally upwards around the central bony column towards its tip. This tissue is known as the spiral ganglion of the acoustic nerve. It connects the cochlea with the brain.

The nerve is thus made up of the long processes or axons of ganglion cells which send their short processes or dendrites to the rows of hair cells on either side of the tunnel of Corti. Each of the inner hair cells seems to be connected with a separate ganglion cell, or two, whereas quite a number of outer hair cells share a ganglion cell between them, each also receiving nerve fibres from more than one ganglion cell. This shared innervation is rather reminiscent of the state of affairs in the retina of the eye, where it has something to do with adaptation to different levels of illumination. Unfortunately, we don't know yet what this means so far as the function of the cochlea is concerned.

Having given you a description of the general lay-out of the sensory part of the cochlea or the organ of Corti, as it is called, I can now return to pursue the sound waves on their way up and down the cochlear spiral in order to see how the whole thing functions.

This gives me an opportunity to demonstrate to you how a wrong theory can produce useful results. I am referring to the so-called resonance theory of Helmholtz. Helmholtz, a great nineteenth-century physicist, was interested in sensory function. His name is often associated with Young's theory of the trichromatic colour vision, but it is in the field of the physiology of hearing that his influence extends to the present day. Helmholtz was struck by the resemblance of the membrana basilaris of the cochlear duct, with its tensioned fibres of increasing length, to the strings of a piano or harp. As you know these, too, are fixed to a frame of roughly triangular shape and range from very short and thin strings for the highest notes to long and thick ones for the lowest base notes. If you depress the sustaining pedal of a piano and sing a certain note into the sound-box, you will hear one of the strings or one of the sets of two or three strings resonate with the sound of your voice. They are the strings that are tuned to the pitch of the note you are singing.

Helmholtz made the assumption that the fibres of the basilar membrane act like tuned strings and that they can therefore resonate each with a certain well-defined frequency of sound. When the fibres resonate in this way, they vibrate and shake the arches of Corti resting on them up and down. The hair cells leaning on such an arch and on no others are rubbed against the overlying membrana tectoria, and this causes their hair processes to bend. The bending or deformation of the hair processes will then, as we have already seen in the case of the ear labyrinth, lead to the excitation of the hair cell and to the discharge of electrical impulses in the sensory nerve branch connected with the hair cell. If the impulses from the hair cells are conducted to the brain in an orderly manner – that is to say, in such a way that the central nervous computer receives accurate information about the exact place along the cochlear duct from which the nerve impulses originate – information becomes available not only about the presence or absence of sound but also about its exact pitch. You see, each part of the cochlea responds to a specific range of frequencies: the base to the highest, the tip to the lowest notes. A chord of three notes will simultaneously excite sensory cells in three different places along the organ of Corti.

Helmholtz's theory can thus be described as a place-representation theory of pitch discrimination and as such can be considered adequate for the functional description of the mechanism involved in the hearing of pitch. On the other hand, the resonance idea on which the theory was originally based has not stood up well to experimental test or further theoretical scrutiny.

To be true resonators, the basilar fibres would have to be free to vibrate independently like the strings of a harp. Instead, they are bound together by the woof of the basilar membrane tissue. In order to resonate over the whole range of the audible spectrum from 16 to 20,000 cycles per second, the longest fibres (which measure roughly half a millimetre), and the shortest (which are of a little more than a tenth part of a millimetre in length) would either have too large a mass or would have to be extremely heavily loaded. The short ones would, on the other hand, have to be under tensions which would tax even the toughest biological materials to the utmost. Investigations into the mass and loading of the fibres and into the tensions obtained in basilar membranes of animals have failed to confirm the existence of such tensions. However, it is certain that the basal end of the cochlear duct is much more rigid than the upper coils, the short fibres being much stiffer than the longer ones.

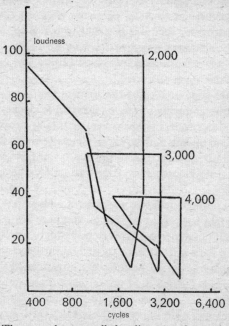

Figure 29. These are three so-called audiograms of acoustic responses of sensory units from the cochlea of a cat. They illustrate that at high intensities each unit responds to a wide range of frequencies. The frequency response becomes, however, fairly narrow and specific near the threshold of audibility. The figures on the left (ordinate) denote arbitrary units of loudness. (*Modified after Galambos and Davis.*)

Finally, experiments in which the sensory impulses were recorded from single sensory units of the organ of Corti in animals have shown that there are no units that respond exclusively to one specific frequency. They all respond to quite a considerable range of frequencies, and this range increases in extent with increasing intensity of sound. The next slide [Figure 29] shows you a number of so-called audiograms in which the width of the frequency response of single sensory units is plotted against intensity. This shows that even near just audible intensities such a single unit responds to a range of notes covering quite a stretch on the piano keyboard. Therefore no such restricted resonance as postulated by Helmholtz occurs in the organ of Corti.

Yet there is no doubt that the organ of Corti analyses pitch by being preferentially sensitive to certain frequencies in certain places, even if the sharpness of tuning postulated by Helmholtz is absent. A man who is exposed to very loud noise in a certain frequency range – say in a boiler factory or shipyard – will develop deafness over a restricted range of pitch corresponding to the frequency spectrum of the damaging noise. If a post-mortem were carried out on his body, it would be found that part of the sensory apparatus of his inner ear is damaged, if not destroyed. This damage would be restricted in good agreement with the tests carried out by specialists, when his complaint of partial deafness was investigated during his lifetime. High-pitched noise would have destroyed a portion of the organ of Corti near the base of the cochlea, noise of lower pitch a portion in its second or third turn. Experiments on animals have fully confirmed this.

As the theory now stands, it seems reasonable to assume that a travelling wave of fluid-conducted sound moves up the cochlea and that this wave throws the cochlear duct into vibratory motion, pushing the basilar membrane rhythmically up and down. When the oval window is pushed inwards, the basilar membrane moves down, and vice versa.

A tone of pure pitch would produce a travelling wave of this kind, the crest of which would finally come to lie within a definite stretch of the cochlea, whose location depends on the frequency of the sound. Within this region many hair cells would in fact be stimulated – the more, the louder the sound – but some would be stimulated more vigorously than others. All the central nervous system has now to do is to pinpoint the place of maximum stimulation along the organ of Corti and compute this in terms of pitch. You may remember how we pondered the way in which the many overlapping tactile nerve endings in the skin could serve in the exact localization of a pin-prick. In that case, too, we demanded that the central nervous system should be able to pinpoint the place of maximum stimulation on a 'map' of the skin. It is on to a central nervous 'map' of the cochlea that the exact pitch of sound must be projected by the incoming signals from the ear. We shall have more to say later about this when we deal with the central nervous end stations [Chapter 10].

A great amount of work is being done in many laboratories to find out what exactly happens in the cochlea, in the auditory nerve, and in the various relay stations between the ear and the final centres of the brain. So far as the cochlea is concerned many attempts have been made to solve some of the functional puzzles by mechanical scale models. These have been useful up to a point, but correct scaling up has proved to be difficult if not impossible.

To end this account of the mode of function of the cochlea, I should like to say a few words about the sensitivity of the ear. First of all, so far as pitch discrimination is concerned, it is interesting that between the frequencies of 16 and 20,000 cycles per second, we can – or, better to say, a musically trained person can – distinguish 1,500 to 2,000 different pure tones. If they were evenly distributed over the range this would mean that, on the average, we can distinguish two notes that differ from one another by about 10 cycles. However, our discrimination is not equally good in the low, middle, and high registers. It is best somewhere in the middle register, where we can in fact distinguish two notes differing only by 1 per cent.

The displacement of the basilar membrane by the softest sound just audible to an observer in an experimental set-up for testing the sensitivity of the ear has been calculated to be as small as 10^{-11} cm. This is a hundred-thousand-millionth part of a centimetre and – this will shake you – amounts to a hundredth part of the diameter of an atom of hydrogen. This calculation is based on a number of assumptions which may or may not be justified. However, even if the displacement of the basilar membrane by a just audible sound were a thousand times greater, it would still be minute; in fact, only ten hydrogen atoms across. You may remember what you learnt about the sensitivity of the eye [p. 63]. The ear can well compete with this!

No wonder this delicate mechanoreceptor has to be protected so well against overstimulation, considering that the sounds it is exposed to range from the rustling of a leaf in the wind to a clap of thunder, to mention only naturally occurring noises. In our civilized life the range is far wider. Taking the rustle of leaves as 10 units above the absolute threshold of hearing, the usual noises at home would cover the range from 20 to 40 units, a normal conversation not degenerating into a row 60, a peal of thunder 70, a railway train or the full blast noise from a radio, to which our kind neighbours expose us in summer through their open windows, 80, and an aeroplane engine at 18 feet distance 120 units. At 140 units above threshold sound inflicts pain instead of being heard in an ordinary sense of the word. Most of these noises cover a wide range of frequencies. A pneumatic hammer at a noise level of 120 units covers a frequency range from 100 to 2,000 cycles, within which the human ear has its highest sensitivity.

This brings me to a matter both of psychological and of medical importance. Many types of noise to which we are nowadays exposed in our daily lives, apart from being annoying and apart from interfering with the efficiency of our work by raising the level of nervous strain, are actually physiologically damaging to our ears. This applies, of course, chiefly to industrial noise. But the noise in a busy office can be equally dangerous, as H. B. Milner points out in an article in *Nature*.* This is a matter of national importance and the Ministry of Pensions and National Insurance has sponsored a large-scale research project for the study of occupational deafness. Apart from this, undue and unwanted noise, especially when it intrudes into public or private life without let or hindrance, is a form of annoyance which people will not tolerate. The recent ban on transistor sets operating in some of Britain's royal parks is a step in the right direction, but only a beginning.

On the other hand, there is the immeasurable joy that can be derived from good music on occasions when our minds are prepared to open themselves to it.

Man as a social animal depends, of course, on hearing for his main method of communication with fellow members of his species. Human speech, as the vehicle for an organized articulate sound-language, is one of the important biological attributes of man and is, to no small measure, responsible for man's progress, since his gradual appearance in the drama of organic evolution roughly a million years ago. The relationship between speech and thought, language and reason has been, and still is, a matter of lively philosophical speculation. But here I am transgressing the boundaries of my topic. The time has come for me to stop and to invite you as usual to ask questions on the topic of the function of the cochlea.

* *Nature*, Volume 204, 338 (1964).

The lecturer answers more questions

STUDENT C: When you spoke of directional hearing, you said you would explain this later in more detail. You haven't said any more about it, and I wonder what sort of time-differences are involved in direction finding.

LECTURER: You are quite right. I did want to say more about this, but I couldn't fit it in. I am therefore glad you ask me this. Differences in the arrival of sound at the two ears vary with the angle the pathway of sound makes with the mid-plane of the head. Sound coming straight from the right will reach the right ear sooner than the left. I know, some of you are interested in actual dimensions. Sound travels in air at 1,100 feet per second. If we assume that the shortest pathway for air-borne sound from ear to ear measures very roughly a foot or so, we find that the time delay in the arrival of sound at our two ears would have to be measured in milliseconds (one millisecond being the thousandth part of a second). It would, of course, be much shorter still in animals with smaller heads. Naturally, the apparent loudness of the sound also differs in both ears, and there are other more sophisticated clues which serve in directional hearing. You will, however, hear a little more about directional hearing in animals on a later occasion.

STUDENT A: What is meant by bone conduction?

LECTURER: The pathway of sound through outer and middle ear, which I described in the lecture, is not the only route by which sound can reach the cochlea. If you put a vibrating tuning fork on the crown of you head, you can hear its sound very well indeed. The bones of your skull are set in vibration, and this in turn excites the organ of Corti, directly bypassing the drum and ear ossicles. This is a clinical method used to find out whether deafness is due to disease in the conducting structures or in the inner ear. Some types of hearing-aid make use of bone conduction, in cases where the middle-ear mechanism is defective. It is interesting in this connexion to remember that quite a lot of animals hear by bone conduction. Snakes do, and the tailed amphibia like newts and salamanders. In some, the sound reaches the inner ear via the bones of the head, in others even through the bones of the fore-limb. Generally speaking, this happens in animals which move close to the ground or in water. Sound reaches them through a solid or fluid medium, and air-borne sound is of no importance.

STUDENT C: I find it difficult to understand what is meant by a travelling wave in the cochlea. All waves travel and I don't see how this can explain why one tone stimulates a certain part of the cochlea maximally and a higher or lower one a different part nearer or farther away from the base.

LECTURER: You are right. The term travelling wave is not a very instructive one. You may remember that I told you that the short fibres of the basilar membrane are much stiffer than the longer ones higher up the coil of the cochlea. That means that the basal end of the cochlear duct is much more rigid and much less yielding than the upper end. When the basal end is thrown into vibration by a passing wave it yields little, but the upper end is 'lashed about' to put it in a vastly exaggerated way – like the thong of a whip cracked by a small but energetic movement of wrist and shaft. The maximum excursion of the thong of the whip would lie at distances from the shaft which would be related to wrist movement. In some such way it is postulated that the greatest bulge in the basilar membrane occurs at a place along its length directly related to the frequency of the disturbance at the base. All model concepts have their strong and weak points, but I think this may help you to visualize the travelling wave in the cochlea. The effect of high frequencies remains confined to the lower turn, and the lowest notes affect all parts of the cochlea with more or less clear maxima at certain places. Do you think this answers your question?

STUDENT C: Thank you. It sounds helpful. I'll think it over.

STUDENT A: Is this all theoretical or have some of the movements been actually observed?

LECTURER: Some of these events have been reproduced in scale-models. The great difficulty lies in the actual process of scaling up, which must not remain confined to the actual size, but must of course extend to masses, densities, viscosities of fluids, conditions of friction, elasticity, tension, and so on. In fact, no scale-model has been made that can be said to reproduce the organ faithfully in all its mechanical properties. And, furthermore, when you have such an enlarged model, your stimulus must be correspondingly scaled, and this is very difficult too. Attempts have, therefore, been made to observe the cochlea itself in the skull, and to look at it under conditions of rapidly interrupted illumination. Such stroboscopic light is used when rapid movements have to be analysed. You may have seen stroboscopic photographs of a high-jumper, of a runner, or even of a rifle bullet in flight. In this way the movements up and down the cochlea in response to changing sound frequencies have been observed microscopically in the exposed cochlea.

STUDENT D: How many hair cells are there in the human cochlea, and are they exactly the same kind of cells as are found in the semicircular canals and in the otolith organs?

LECTURER: I take the second part of your question first. The answer is that the hair cells in the cochlea differ in one important aspect from the vestibular ones. Their hair processes consist of solid cilia or stereocilia only. The kinocilium, which, as you will remember, resembles a motile cilium or flagellum, is absent. Only its root is found embedded in the top layer of the cell, but no hair process grows out of it.

What this difference means is completely obscure at present. There is also a difference in the relationship with the covering structure. The hair processes of the sensory cells in the ear labyrinth are embedded in their cupulae or in the otolith membranes, whereas it very much looks as if the hair processes of the cochlear hair cells only touch the tectorial membrane with their tips. What else did you want to know?

STUDENT D: I asked how many cells there are in the human cochlea.

LECTURER: Oh yes. Let me see. Here it is. There are about 3,500 inner hair cells. These are bigger than the outer hair cells of which there are about 20,000. There are about 28,000 nerve cells in the spiral ganglion of the cochlea.

STUDENT D: What is the size of the hair cells?

LECTURER: The inner hair cells have a diameter of 12μ, the outer of 8μ only. We don't really know what this means. Altogether we know very little yet about the way these cells function. All we know is that they transduce a mechanical deformation of the hair processes into a coded electrical signal in the nerves connecting them with the central nervous system.

STUDENT B: Is there any correspondence between the frequency of the sound and, presumably, with the frequency of bending of the hair processes and the number of nerve impulses fired into the acoustic nerve fibres?

LECTURER: This is an important question. Let us start with notes of high frequency – say 20,000 cycles per second. No nerve fibre can fire at that rate. [See Introduction, p. 19.] As each nerve impulse is followed by a period during which the nerve is inexcitable, and as this so-called refractory period lasts a millisecond or so, and the impulse itself lasts about the same time or somewhat longer, no normal nerve can be expected to fire faster than several hundred to a thousand times a second. This explains why animals responding to high-pitched sound are equipped with an organ like the cochlea, in which frequency and place along the organ are related in the way I have described. Of course, neighbouring hair cells could work together in groups in such a way that each member only responds to every second, third, fourth, and so on vibration, while together such a group might in this way accurately transmit frequencies of a few thousand cycles per second. This has, in fact, been postulated to account for the fact that a bundle of fibres can be observed to reproduce such stimulus frequencies. But this sort of transmission, which is called frequency-synchronized transmission, goes haywire at still higher frequencies. I shall mention frequency-synchronized transmission again when I come to describe hearing in fishes and in insects [Chapter 8].

STUDENT E: This worries me. I thought that nerve impulses are always coded in such a way that their frequency is a function of the intensity of the stimulus. I am quite sure this is what we were told. How does the central nervous system disentangle this, when the frequency of impulse coming from the ear is now supposed to carry information about the pitch of the stimulating sound?

LECTURER: You are quite right. There is an apparent contradiction. We have to assume that the computing centre in the brain which deals with the cochlea, or with the sound receptors in the fish-ear, is specially programmed to cope with this.

STUDENT E: But, even if this were so, how does the brain know how loud the stimulating sound is?

LECTURER: We believe that in this case loudness or intensity is gauged by the total number of nerve fibres stimulated. If we assume that the receptor units vary in their sensitivity, then a soft sound will stimulate a few only, a loud sound a greater number of receptors in a given part of the cochlea. This is as far as I can go. Here, as always, our knowledge is incomplete, and much is still hypothetical. I am afraid our time is up. May I say how pleased I am with the high standard of your questions.

8

HEARING IN ANIMALS

ENOUGH of the classroom! Let us now consider the question of hearing in our fellow animals. There is no doubt that the mammals have developed the use of air-borne acoustic information to a high pitch in every sense of the word. Their sensitivity ranges wide, both on the intensity and on the frequency scale. In this respect it would be a mistake to choose man as the measure of things. A cat hears frequencies up to 50,000 cycles, and a bat's ear reaches up to 120,000 cycles. Many animals can localize sound direction much more accurately than we, and have probably a significantly higher sensitivity to soft sound. After all, the primates, to whom we belong, are day-active animals, enjoying the fullest benefit of visual orientation, including the rich source of information derived from colour vision. The rest of our fellow mammals depend on their sense of smell and on hearing in dealing with the dangers and pleasures of life which are most actively encountered and pursued at dusk, dawn, or even during the night.

Sonar

Yet the astonishing extension of the audible sound spectrum to 120,000 cycles found in bats cannot be readily understood by a necessity for listening in to the noises made during flight by their air-borne insect prey. Those noises lie in a much lower range of the frequency spectrum. The astonishing fact is that bats use their acoustic faculties for listening to their own high-pitched squeaks. And when I say their own, I mean that each bat listens to its own vocal performance and not to that of its fellow bats. Why? This is certainly not a spectacular case of narcissism among animals – but a most ingenious mechanism of vocal-acoustic echo-sounding.

As early as 1794 Spallanzani demonstrated that bats, when flying about in the dark, never bump into obstacles, and that they can locate and pounce upon insect prey with uncanny aim while both they and their prey fly at great speed. We now know that they do this by emitting pulsed shrieks of very high frequency of which only a small portion is audible to us. Most of the sound produced has frequencies between 25,000 and 110,000 cycles. Such high-frequency sound is reflected from small objects much more accurately than sound of lower pitch, almost like light from a torch. We now see why an extension of the upper limit of hearing is of such great value that it has been evolved in bats with all the necessary dimensional and functional changes in the hearing apparatus. The cochlea of a bat looks different from the ordinary run of mammalian cochleae. The organ of Corti is more compact and rigid, and there are a number of modifications in the lay-out which are all physically geared to high-tone hearing. Interestingly enough we find some quite similar modifications in the inner ear of whales and dolphins, and they, too, have extended upper-frequency hearing for precisely the same reason as the bats. They also echo-locate. But they do it in water where one of the great assets of bats – namely, highly motile and outsize ear-flaps – would be of little use to them (Chapter 7).

But let us finish the story of the bat before we descend to the sea to join the whales and porpoises. There are among the small insect-eating bats two types which differ in the way they echo-locate. They are the vespertilionids with relatively small ears and the horseshoe bats with very large highly motile ears and with a horseshoe-shaped nasal organ used for sound projection. The vespertilionid bats are cosmopolitan bats quite common in this country. They produce ultrasonic bursts of sound accompanied by clicks audible to us. The ultrasonic sound consists of very short explosion-like groups of sound waves of declining frequency starting at say 90,000 cycles and dropping rapidly to about 25,000 cycles. Each such burst lasts only one to three thousandths of a second and there may be three hundred such bursts per second. The repetition rate is continuously variable. It is low when the bat is just aimlessly flying about, but becomes faster during exploration or during the chase of a prey. We have heard of a similar speed-up in signal emission in the case of the electric fish (Chapter 4). The sound is produced in the larynx and is emitted through the mouth. One needs special instruments to make the ultrasonic impulses audible to the human observer, and it is an interesting experience to see and hear a bat chase an insect. The American zoologist Griffin, who has studied these bats intensively, has made a sound film in colour showing a bat chasing its prey lit up in the beam of photoflood bulbs, so that one can see bat and prey, and at the same time hear the ever more rapidly repeated orientation cries fired off by the bat in a crescendo of frequency, whenever the hunter is on target and stopping, when the prey is caught in its wings used as nets. This film is among the most exciting biological films ever made.

The title of Griffin's book – *Listening in the Dark* – is an eloquent description of the behaviour of animals that can be said to be 'all ear' and to have 'image hearing' as we have 'image vision'. It is difficult for us to imagine how these agile animals hear the world in utter darkness by the search-beams of sound produced by their own larynx. Think of the accurate computing of time-differences that is necessary to estimate the time which elapses between the emission of a sound burst and its reception by the ear! And for direction hearing, for which in these bats the collaboration of both ears is necessary, the difference in the time of arrival of the sound at one and the other ear is extremely small, a matter of microseconds. We must assume that the bat's brain must be able to utilize a number of additional clues such as the difference in loudness or even in the phase of the sound in the two ears and their relationship to the direction whence the echo reaches it.

There are quite a number of such tricky problems involved in the analysis of echo-sounding, or sonar, in bats. For instance, how can a bat, while it emits such a volley of cries, distinguish between the cries leaving through the mouth and the cries reflected from an outside object? We have to assume that the bat's ears are shielded somehow from its own sounds. In that case the accurate time of emission must be somehow recorded directly in the brain. These are difficult problems which are still being studied by means of refined experimental techniques. If the mouth of such a bat is closed by a bandage or if one or both the ears are plugged, the animal is absolutely helpless and, if induced to fly at all, it bumps into even large objects. Normally it can fly dexterously through a webwork of thin threads without getting caught in it, and is able to distinguish from a distance the nature of a surface, say velvet from wood or glass! The one 'sounds' softer, rougher, or smoother than the other!

The horseshoe bats use the bizarre appendages of their nostrils as megaphones, keeping their mouths closed when they emit their orientation cries. These cries have a constant unmodulated frequency of about 100,000 cycles and last much longer than the vespertilionid cries – namely, up to a tenth of a second. The intervals between such cries are rather short. They are therefore not very well suited for the computation of the time-difference between emission and reception of the echo. It is here that the rather large and highly motile ear-flaps of the horseshoe bats come into the picture. These ears carry out constant scanning movements of a complex spatial pattern and each of them alone is sufficient for echo-sounding, while a vespertilionid bat with one ear plugged is pretty disorientated. It thus seems that loudness differences between echoes form the chief directional clues for horseshoe bats. Dr Möhres, who has chiefly studied horseshoe bats, believes that their system of echo-sounding – using the nose as a directional ultrasound projector and the continuously roving ears as loudness scanners – represents the highest perfection of sonar in the animal kingdom. Some workers disagree with Möhres and believe that comparison of loudness is not the chief mechanism in horseshoe bats. Making use of acoustic models they have come to the conclusion that the so-called Doppler effect helps them in gauging whether they are approaching an object or receding from it. It is common experience that the pitch of the whistle of a railway engine sharpens when the train approaches and becomes flat when it rushes away from us. A bat flying up or down the echo beam of its ultrasonic orientation cries may thus hear their pitch rise or fall as the case may be, the change in pitch indicating the whereabouts of the object.

Some large fruit-eating bats also echo-locate. Besides, they orientate by means of good night vision and a very acute sense of smell. Cave swiftlets and oil birds are birds which spend their lives in dark caves. They echo-locate by lower-frequency sounds which are audible to us. They also have good night vision. A search is at present being conducted among other nocturnal animals such as hamsters, dormice, shrews, and rats for the possible use of sonar besides other means of orientation. No reliable evidence has so far been obtained.

Whales and dolphins don't see very well and when swimming under water at great speed they, too, use sonar. Whales have, of course, no external ears. Ear-flaps would interfere with streamlining and would be absolutely useless for sound localization under water. The middle ear is highly modified. The meatus is solid, but has been shown to conduct sound better than the surrounding tissues. The drum is modified into a flat triangular band of tissue attached with its pointed end to the ossicle chain of hammer, anvil, and stirrup. These bones are also somewhat modified in shape and lead to the oval window. The basilar membrane is very narrow at the basal end and this suggests high-frequency hearing. We have already learnt (Chapter 7) that in whales the bone containing the inner ear is freely suspended from the skull by ligaments and is completely surrounded by air spaces. This insulation of the two ears from one another helps directional hearing, by making the two ears acoustically independent. Whales and dolphins are sensitive to sound up to 100,000 cycles, and they utter high-pitched cries. It has been quite definitely established that they use ultrasound in echo-location. That they can hear ultrasound became disappointingly obvious when the post-war whaling fleets attempted to locate whales by sonar in much the same way as the submarine hunters had done during the war in search of enemy submarines. The whalers soon realized that their quarry heard the sonar signals, took fright and escaped before they could be tracked down.

Sonar is one of the achievements in the development of which for navigational purposes man was little aided by biological knowledge. In fact, the analysis of echo-location in bats, birds, and whales was greatly helped by the advances made by engineers, especially by those made under the pressure of war. More recently, however, the more refined methods of navigational sonar are beginning to benefit in their development by what we have learnt from bats. Sonar aids for blind people are now being developed. In these the lessons learnt from bats find practical application. At the same time the designers have discovered certain features of echo-location which are, in turn, of considerable help in the interpretation of animal sonar systems. When, at the beginning of the Second World War, radar entered the field of air defence and later became a means of accurate target recognition in night bombing, the development engineer had no animal prototype to help him. The principles of radar and sonar are rather similar except for the enormous differences in the nature of the signal: electromagnetic waves in radar, sound waves in sonar. The actual dimensions of the waves used in these two systems are in fact rather similar. In radar we use electromagnetic waves in the centimetre band, and the wavelengths of bat cries are measured in fractions of a centimetre. The similarity is not accidental. In order to be of use in the spotting of small, relatively near objects or larger but far distant ones, a signal beam must have directional qualities. Light, of course, with its wavelengths measured in millimicrons is by far the best signal for orientation.

Distant touch

A much clumsier, yet quite efficient, location system, based on the principle of sending out a signal and receiving back a reflection of it, is used by fish. They have a sense organ known as lateral line in which sensory hair cells are lodged in fluid-filled canals which open through pores to the surrounding water. These canals are distributed along a pattern of lines extending all over the head and down the flanks of the body. Small water movements, caused either by the fish itself during swimming and then reflected back over short distances on to its head and body, or other animals moving about in the vicinity of the fish, move the fluid in the lateral-line canals. The configuration of strength and direction of the movement of the canal fluid enables the fish to locate the obstacle or the moving object in its vicinity. The movement of the canal fluid stimulates the hair cells just as we have seen in the case of semicircular canals of the ear. It cannot be emphasized too strongly that the water movements involved in this method of mechano-location have nothing to do with sound. Sound is propagated by pressure waves. Here we deal with bodily movements of water away from and towards the body of the fish. No satisfactory experimental evidence has been obtained for an acoustic function of the lateral line, but its sensitivity to water movement is remarkable and very small disturbances of the water can be accurately localized by fish with what has been called the sense of distant touch.

What fish can hear

We now know for certain that fish can hear in the true sense of the word. Some of them not only hear over a considerable range of the sound-frequency spectrum (up to 4,000 cycles) but they also have fairly accurate pitch discrimination in the lower-frequency range up to 800 cycles. All this has been analysed and scientifically substantiated during the last thirty years or so. Earlier on, fish were believed to be deaf, because their inner ears lack a cochlea and because there is no trace of an outer or middle ear. The inner ear was thought to serve exclusively the sense of balance and posture (Chapter 6). To test the validity of the assumption of deafness in fish, investigators played musical instruments in front of aquaria. Even a coloratura soprano was invited to sing to them on account of the very wide range of her voice. As expected, the results of these tests were negative. The fish did not react to the musical 'treats' provided for them. Despite what fisherman's lore would claim, fish were apparently as stone deaf as the anatomists predicted. The trouble with these investigations was, of course, that the stimulus presented had no biological significance for the fish despite its unquestionable aesthetic human value.

Things changed when the Pavlovian method of conditioning or training was brought to bear on the problem. In Chapter 4 such an experiment on a fish was outlined. With the help of this method the hearing power of fish was fully established.

The question then arose: what do fish hear with? This was answered by a series of delicate and difficult experiments, in which it could be shown that the sense of hearing is localized in parts of the inner ear, more specifically in one or the other of the otolith organs. In Chapter 6 we observed an electrophysiological experiment on a semicircular canal in the vestibular organ of a ray. In a similar type of experiment on the otolith organ in the sacculus of the same fish, it can be shown that this part of the inner ear does not, like the utriculus, react to change of position in space. Instead, it reacts very sensitively to vibration, at least up to 120 cycles. Each hair cell makes the nerve fibre connected with it fire at the frequency of the stimulus. We may therefore assume that in bony fish, which hear much better than sharks and rays, one or the other otolith organ which is specially exposed to sound waves functions as a sound receptor. The specifically heavy otolith may be thought of as furnishing an inert resistance, against which the hair processes of the sensory cell are rocked to and fro when the sound waves reach the tissues of the inner ear. In the cyprinoid bony fish, which are 'top' in hearing among all fishes, the air bladder acts as a resonator, and a chain of three bones, the Weberian ossicles, forms a solid bridge between the air bladder and the fluid-filled otolith organ of the inner ear. The physics of the matching process between water-borne sound and the solid otolith are very complicated and we must skip them.

But – it may be asked – is there really a lot of sound under water? The answer is: yes, a surprising amount. Fish are not deaf, but they are not quite mute either. Sound production in fish is very common indeed, and the various devices used by fish for making a noise are a fascinating object of biological study made nowadays with underwater microphones of high sensitivity and fidelity. Sound up to a frequency of 400 to 500 cycles is used by fish for species recognition and for sexual display. But many other aquatic animals produce sound apart from fishes. Shrimps and other crustaceans are a very noisy lot indeed and, last but not least, aquatic mammals like whales and dolphins contribute to the chorus both in the audible and in the supersonic range. There are recordings available now which demonstrate the concerted 'vocal' efforts of shoals of certain species of fish that can rival the best dawn chorus of our native birds.

Hearing in birds

By the way, we have not said much about hearing in birds. The counterpart of the mammalian cochlea is the papilla basilaris in the ear of birds. Birds, for the sake of staking territorial claims and for a number of other reasons, are highly vocal animals. They also hear well. Their frequency range of hearing is more restricted, but by and large their papilla basilaris functions as well as the mammalian cochlea, although it has a much simpler structure. It has no organ of Corti nor a division of hair cells into rows of inner and outer ones.

A lot of work has in recent years been done in which the frequency content of bird-song has been analysed by means of so-called sound-spectrographs. The complex nature of bird calls and songs makes it certain that recognition of bird by bird makes a high perfection of pitch-discrimination an absolute necessity.

An interesting difference exists between warning calls with which one rather alert bird, acting as a sentinel, warns a whole population of birds of his own and other species of the approach of danger, and the various songs by means of which male birds advertise their presence and inform all and sundry of the sanctity of their territory including the females residing in it.

Warning calls consist of high-pitched and simple sound sequences which are striking and yet difficult to localize. They don't give away the whereabouts of the sentinel. The truculent lower-pitched territory-marking songs, on the other hand, have a highly directional quality and accurately pinpoint the very tree from which they are broadcast.

All this means that birds should be very good in acoustic direction-finding. Yet they have no outer ear-flaps and their ears are close together in their little heads. To make up for this, birds can swivel their heads about rapidly in all directions, and these many different and attractive movements and postures of the head serve in the visual and in acoustic exploration of space.

Stridulation and hearing in insects

When one travels in subtropical and tropical countries one is struck day and night by the incessant chirping and singing of cicadas and other insects. This sound background is so typical that a producer of a play on film or TV trying to depict a scene under southern skies could not possibly afford to omit dubbing it into the sequences shot in a London studio. These insect calls serve in the finding of mates and in territory marking.

All manner of sound-producing structures are used by insects. They are known as stridulating organs, and consist in principle of hard resonating structures which are rhythmically rubbed against each other. Wings and legs serve both as fiddles and fiddle bows. The range of pitch of these stridulating sounds is wide, and they extend far into the high-frequency and ultrasonic range.

It is quite certain that insects which produce all this noise must also be able to hear it. Their 'ears' are strange organs found in all sorts of unlikely places, such as in legs and in the abdomen. Rows of vibration-sensitive sensory organs are arranged in the vicinity of air sacs which act as resonators.

Such ears are called tympanic organs (Figure 30). It has been shown that the tympanic organs of insects are not only highly sensitive but are most excellent direction finders. Sensory impulses conducted in the tympanic nerves have been recorded

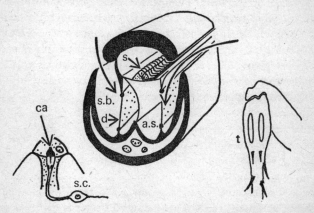

Figure 30. This shows a thick cross-section of the tibial segment of the fore-leg of a grasshopper. The tibia (t) situated below the knee-joint has two slit-like openings. These are marked in the enlarged cross-section by the curved arrows which indicate the pathway of sound waves into the cavities of the 'ear'. The core of the tibia is partly hollow and contains large air sacs (a.s.) which are part of the tracheal system. Drum-like membranes (d) are tightly spread across the outside of these tracheal sacs and separate the tracheal air space from the sound box (s.b.). On top of the air sacs a longitudinal ridge of sensory cells (s) is balanced in such a way that the vibrations conducted to it via the sound boxes and drums stimulate the sensory cells rhythmically by mechanical deformation. One such sensory cell (s.c.) is shown in higher magnification and can be seen to contain a typical cap and peg structure (ca) at the end.

in response to actual calls from a male of the same species. The pattern of electric impulses accurately reproduces the rhythmical pattern of the chirping, but not the actual frequency of the stridulation sound which carries the staccato rhythm of the endlessly repeated call. This situation can be likened to what happens in sound radio. We do not hear the frequency of what is called the carrier wave, on the back of which speech or music travels to us from all over the world. We hear the pattern of sound that has been moulded on to the carrier wave, or by which this wave has been modulated, as the engineer would say. Something similar happens when we make a telephone call over a bad line. A lot of the 'music' in the voice of our caller can be lost and yet we are still able to understand what is said by recognizing the rhythmical pattern of words.

Hearing a socializing factor

We must by now be impressed by the enormous importance sound has in communication in animals and man. It is one of the great socializing factors by which individuals of a species are welded together in their common activities. What would man be without speech? It can be said that speech has perhaps been the most important factor in man's progress from a solitary browser and hunter to a builder of complex civilizations. Such progress is based on collaboration and on the handing on from individual to individual of information in the form of precisely shaped, easily recognizable and reproducible signals: words in a system of grammar. It has even been said that human thought, as we know it, has evolved from speech. Whether this is true or not, hearing, however inferior in acuteness and range it may be as compared with what we find in some of our fellow animals, has helped man perhaps more than any other factor besides vision to become the master of his destiny.

9

THE CHEMICAL SENSE

What is taste?

THIS chapter is being written under the glowing impression of Christmas fare. Tasty foods and the aroma of seasonal drinks linger in the memory. And yet there must have been – at this time of the year – many unfortunates for whom, having caught a cold in the head, all this tasted like cardboard and water! This is of course an exaggeration born from the miserable outlook on life that goes with a cold in the head. Unless a cold is accompanied by a raving fever, it will not interfere with 'taste' as such. Sweet, salty, sour, bitter, corrosive, and, strangely enough, rough, smooth, soft and crisp, cool and warm can still be appreciated. Among these only the first four or five belong to the province of the chemical sense. The others are part of our response to mechanical stimuli, but they definitely enter into our appreciation and enjoyment of food and drink. What our disgruntled patients missed was the addition of the complex symphony of scents that go with what we commonly call the 'taste' of things. These they could not appreciate, because their noses were blocked and their sense of smell temporarily on strike.

The sense organs responsible for distinguishing sweet from salt, sour from bitter, bitter from salt and sweet, sweet and salt from sour are lodged in microscopically small pits and grooves on our tongue. Some are found in other parts of the mouth, too, but the tongue is our chief taster. They are secondary sensory cells looking superficially like the sensory cells in the ear, except that the hair-like processes on their tip are much shorter and blunter. The bodies of these so-called gustatory cells are spun round with the endings of the tongue nerves, which are branches of the seventh and ninth brain nerves.

This simple anatomical fact draws a strict line of demarcation between the taste organs associated with the mouth and the organs of smell in the nose. Its nerve processes enter the foremost part of the brain through a nerve tract commonly known as the first nerve. Like the second nerve which comes from the eye, this is not a nerve at all but part of the brain itself. Thus information about taste and smell is carried to widely different centres lying at the front and at the back of the brain respectively.

In the light of what we know about colour vision and about the hearing of pitch, we must naturally wonder whether the distinction of four or five qualities of taste calls for the presence on the tongue of four or five different types of chemo-sensitive cells. We certainly have no reason to believe that such different cells, if they existed, would differ recognizably in their appearance under the microscope. In fact, like the cones in the retina, all taste cells look the same. However, the sensitivity for the four chief taste qualities is distributed over the surface of our tongue in an interesting pattern. This is shown in Figure 31. The position of the receptors for bitter explains why we try to swallow a bitter pill quickly before it can come into prolonged contact with the back of our tongue. How much sweeter things taste at the tip, and how a sour orange makes the side of the tongue try to curl away from it!

The sensory cells are arranged in groups known as taste buds sunk below the surface of the tongue into pits and grooves. There are secretory cells associated with the taste buds. Their watery secretions rinse the pits and grooves, making them ever-ready to receive new and varied stimuli.

The uneven distribution of sensitivity for various tastes all over the tongue means that, despite their similarity in appearance, there may be taste cells which are specifically sensitive to one or the other quality or at least to a specific group of qualities. Here an electrophysiological study of the nervous messages travelling along the taste nerves might give us some more information. Such experiments have been carried out

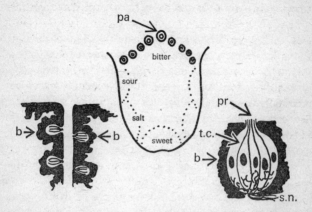

Figure 31. This shows the human tongue and its areas of specific sensitivity to sweet, salt, sour, and bitter. At its base there is a row of wart-like papillae (pa), each surrounded by a circular furrow. In the walls of such a furrow are lodged the so-called taste buds (b). One of them is shown more highly magnified and can be seen to consist of taste cells (t.c.) which receive at their base the end branches of a sensory nerve (s.n.). In this respect the taste cells resemble the secondary sensory cells found in the ear and in the lateral line. However, they lack the elongated hair processes characteristic for the cells of the acoustico-lateralis system. Instead, they have short stumpy processes (pr) which project just a little into the fluid-filled space of the furrow.

on human patients in whom one branch of the nerve supply of the tongue, the chorda tympany, had to be exposed during operations on the ear. In similar experiments on cats it could be shown that there are specific units responding to acid and salt or to bitter only. Cats do not seem to be sensitive to sweet substances at all. This fits in well with the fact that you cannot endear yourself to a cat by bribing it with lumps of sugar. In some cases units could be isolated that showed a good response only to pure water, which must therefore be counted among the tasting substances. As we shall find presently, this rather astonishing discovery has been confirmed in experiments on insects.

Chemists, physicists, and, of course, biologists have tried to find out why it is that one kind of substance tastes salty and another sweet, acid, or bitter. What have all salty or sweet substances in common? It is easiest with sour substances. They are usually compounds which the chemist calls acids, because they contain charged hydrogen atoms which can be dissociated from them in watery solution. The sour taste has in fact been attributed to these hydrogen ions, as they are called. However, hydrochloric acid tastes sour only in fairly dilute form, and the much more pronounced sour taste of citric acid cannot be wholly explained by its content of hydrogen ions, of which it contains fewer than dilute hydrochloric or sulphuric acid. Common salt is the chloride of sodium. The question arises whether its salty taste is caused by sodium or by chlorine. Neither is exclusively the case. There are salty chlorides without sodium, and salty sodium compounds without chlorine. Things are still more complicated in the case of sweet substances. They cover a very wide range of chemical substances of completely different molecular form and constitution.

Cane sugar, glucose, and milk sugar taste unequally sweet. Cane sugar is the sweetest. Yet their chemical constitution is very much alike. Saccharine, on the other hand, is a coal-tar derivative of completely different constitution. It is seven hundred times sweeter than cane sugar. Salts of lead also taste sweet, and there is precious little resemblance between their molecules and a molecule of sugar.

What is still more tantalizing is that we cannot as yet

imagine what exactly happens when a tasting substance interacts with a gustatory cell, and how it is that certain cells
should be tuned in to one or the other type of substance. The
solution of this problem will be a matter of close collaboration
between biochemists, biophysicists, and biologists. It is bound
to involve complex analytical work. In this the study of the
ultrastructure of the membrane and contents of the receptor
cells by means of the electron-microscope may have to play a
vital part.

How does the sensitivity of our taste receptors compare with
those ultra-sensitive sensory cells in eye and ear? Overall sensitivities are not high in man, and there are great individual
differences. The values for solutions in water that can just be
spotted by an average human observer are fifty parts in a
million of hydrochloric acid, five parts in ten thousand of
common salt, seven parts in a thousand of saccharine, and
about the same concentration of quinine. When asked to
estimate the strength of two solutions of the same substance a
30 per cent difference is usually just recognizable. We shall
see presently that some animals have a much more acute sense
of taste.

What is the biological advantage of taste? Obviously, even
primitive man, although being a visual animal and therefore
relying chiefly on visual memory of shape and colour in the
discrimination between palatable and poisonous foods, can be
reminded of previous ill-effects by a bitter taste, or sweetness
may lead him to eat energy-rich food. But these factors are
usually very obvious and far above the just noticeable level.
Besides, scents are more efficient advertisements of quality,
especially as they act over a distance. Detection of saltiness in
traces may, however, have had survival value even in man and,
of course, much more so in our fellow mammals, who can experience physiologically dangerous salt lack under certain
circumstances. Salt is a precious commodity in primitive

human society, and big game are known to make spectacular migrations in search of salt.

In fish, taste buds are not confined to the mouth cavity but are found all over the body embedded in the slimy skin. Fish, therefore, taste with their whole body surface. It is not surprising therefore that their sensitivity for certain substances far surpasses our own. A trained minnow, for instance, can distinguish the four standard taste qualities from one another in quite astonishingly dilute solutions. It is, for instance, sixty times more sensitive to sugar than man.

Like all backboned animals, fish have noses. Their noses are still much more highly sensitive than their taste buds.

The sense of smell

However, before we deal with the sense of smell in fish, let us have a look at our own noses. They are quite pronounced, as noses go, forgetting for the moment the snout of a pig or the trunk of an elephant. The prominent size of our nose is misleading. We do not excel in olfactory sensitivity among our fellow mammals. In fact, we and the other primates are probably surpassed by all of them. Most mammals, being nocturnal, use their sense of smell for orientation as well as in the search for food or for spotting friend and foe, mate or rival. The nose is the inlet and outlet for the air we breathe, and surprisingly little of this air normally reaches the layer of sensory cells tucked away in the convolutions of the nasal conch in the turbinate bone of our skull (Figure 32). Only eddies from the main stream of air float over the sensory cells, except when we or any spooring animal deliberately sniff air up and down rather violently. Scent-carrying substances reach the 'inner nose' in very small quantities. The proportion of surface of the 'inner nose' covered by sensory cells is an indication of the acuteness of smell in an animal. It is strikingly larger in a dog or deer than in man. Nevertheless, it would be a mistake to underrate man's sensitivity by judging it on the basis of our own experience. Modern civilized man does not use his nose much. Certainly it is not used for orientation in finding our way about the streets of a city, except by a blind man who wants to make sure he has spotted the entrance of his restaurant

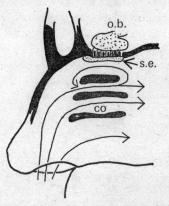

Figure 32. This shows a human nose in section. The arrows indicate the pathway of respiratory air through the folds of the conch (co). It can be seen that an eddy-current of air runs through the topmost fold of the conch where the sensory epithelium is situated (s.e.). The sensory cells send their nerve processes through sieve-like pores in the base of the skull into the olfactory bulb (o.b.) of the brain.

correctly. Continental Europeans derive more enjoyment from scents than inhabitants of the British Isles, where a 'perfumed person' is regarded with a certain amount of suspicion. One sometimes wonders whether the climate may have something to do with this. On the other hand, it is quite clear that aborigines such as bushmen, who have to fend for themselves under severe conditions of scarcity of food and water, must use their sense of smell to an extent not much different from that found in nocturnal mammals. A dog's world is a world of scents, and it is difficult for us to imagine an environment in which objects are recognizable by their scent and not by their shape and colour. Someone once said that a composer

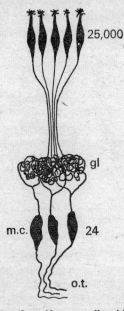

Figure 33. This shows a few olfactory cells with their hair processes. Their nerve processes run in bundles to the olfactory bulb. Here they enter the so-called glomeruli (gl.) Each of these receives about 25,000 sensory nerve fibres which synapse in the glomerulus with the dendritic processes of about twenty-four so-called mitral cells (m.c.), and with the processes of about sixty tufted cells not shown in the diagram. All the axons of the mitral cells form the olfactory tract (o.t.), whereas those of the tufted cells make connexion with the opposite side of the brain.

bent on giving his dog an aesthetic treat would have to write a symphony of scents for him, to be performed on an organ giving forth chords of scent instead of sound. How many notes would make up the melodies and harmonies of such a composition?

Even the number of scents that are distinguished by our 'blunt' sense of smell is bewilderingly large. A perfumer's catalogue may contain many hundreds of different scents. It is obviously impossible that there should be as many different receptors as there are different scents. Let us have a look at the receptors (Figure 33). They are, like the rods and cones of the retina, so-called primary sensory cells with a tuft of cilia at the top and a nerve process continuous with the cell body. They are arranged in a yellow-pigmented patch of the slimy nasal coating. The cilia are embedded in the slimy nasal fluid and have been observed to carry out slow movements rather reminiscent of the slow opening and closing of the petals of a flower in a time-lapse film. The sensory cells are held in position by supporting cells. Between the supporting cells are also found free nerve endings belonging to the fifth brain nerve. These are sensitive to strong chemical fumes like ammonia and acids and also to mechanical stimuli. The nerve processes from the olfactory receptor cells are extremely thin. They run in closely packed bundles through a sieve-like part of the nasal bone to a part of the fore-brain known as the olfactory bulb. In the bulb are so-called glomeruli, where the sensory fibres make connexion with the processes of so-called mitral cells. Each mitral cell receives roughly a thousand olfactory nerve endings, but has itself only one long nerve process which runs through the olfactory tract to the olfactory lobe of the fore-brain. There is, therefore, a great amount of cross-connexion between the sensory cells by the mitral cells each collecting information from a great number of receptors. This, again, is reminiscent of the cross-connexions in the retina.

A new hypothesis

It would be a fitting illustration of how far we are from understanding olfactory function to enumerate here the many theories that have been thought up in the attempt to explain, first of all, the incredibly high sensitivity of the nasal cells, and further the fact that we and animals in general can distinguish so many different scents. None of these theories has yielded a consistent picture in which the chemical composition of the odoriferous substances is fully correlated with their different effect on our nose. However, patient sorting out and comparison of hosts of odoriferous substances seems at last to have yielded a basis for an explanation of scent discrimination. It is probably not the chemical composition of the molecules of odoriferous substances, but their overall shape that may be at the root of scent discrimination. Dr Amoore and collaborators in America have been able to group scents into seven categories which they call primary odours. These are camphoraceous, musky, floral, pepperminty, etherial, pungent, and putrid. It is claimed that all known scents are one or the other of these, or combinations of two, three, or more primary odours. In this hypothesis specific odours such as that of cedar-wood oil have in fact been reconstructed by mixtures of substances with pure camphoraceous, musky, floral, and pepperminty scents.

The promising aspect of this work is that we have now got to look out not for thousands of different receptor sites in the nose but only for about seven. Combinations of these could then be stimulated by various substances of different compound odours. The central nervous computer would have to elaborate a different scent image for each of these stimulus patterns. This again is reminiscent of what happens in colour vision, where we assume that there are only three different receptor sites, each specifically sensitive to one of the three primary colours.

The new hypothesis goes farther. In an attempt to link molecular shape to primary odour it was found that many molecules having any such primary odour have the same characteristic overall shape. These shapes are illustrated in Figure 34. It is assumed that the seven different receptor sites in the sensitive portions of the olfactory cells have themselves shapes into which the molecules of odoriferous substances fit. When such a site is occupied by a molecule, excitation of the olfactory

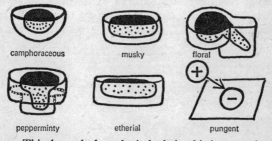

Figure 34. This shows the hypothetical relationship between the shape of receptor sites for olfactory stimulation and the molecular shape of six of the fundamental odoriferous substances. In the case of substances with pungent scent, site selection is a matter of electric charge rather than molecular shape. (*Modified after Amoore* et al.)

cell may be triggered off. It is an open question whether there are seven different types of olfactory cells each with receptor sites of one shape only, or whether more than one site can be found on sensory cells. Of course, even if this hypothesis were a real break-through we shall still have to find out how the chemical events connected with the fitting of the scent molecule into the receptor site lead to the firing of the nervous signal and how this signal is coded. With this question we have arrived at exactly the same point at the frontier of knowledge at which our inquiries into the mechanism of all the other senses ended.

One very curious thing must be mentioned. As Dr Amoore

and his collaborators point out, one of the earliest attempts at explaining the difference in the scent of various substances, made by the pre-Socratic Greek nature philosophers Leucippus and Democritus, was summarized by the Roman poet Lucretius (see Chapter 10). He attributed differences in taste to differences in the shape of atoms. Lucretius, like any naïve observer, does not distinguish between taste and smell and says:

The liquids of honey and milk have a pleasant taste as they are moved about in the mouth; but contrariwise the loathsome nature of wormwood and of harsh centaury twists up the mouth with a noisome flavour; so that you may readily recognize that those bodies which touch our senses pleasantly are made of smooth and round atoms, but contrariwise all that seem to be bitter and rough are held in connection by atoms more hooked, and are therefore wont to tear open their way into our senses and to break the texture by their intrusion.*

And again in another place:

In the first place we perceive flavour in the mouth while we squeeze it out in munching the food, as if one haply takes in hand a sponge full of water and begins to press it dry. Then that which we squeeze out is distributed abroad through all the channels of the palate and the contorted passages of the tongue. Therefore when the bodies of the oozing juice are smooth, sweetly they touch and sweetly stroke all the wet trickling regions around the tongue. But contrariwise they prick the sense and tear it as soon as they arise, in proportion as they *are* more full of roughness.†

This sounds pretty naïve, and yet it is at least an intriguing state of affairs that we in the twentieth century A.D. still speculate about the chemical sense in terms of the molecular shape.

* *De rerum natura* (trans. W. H. D. Rouse, Heinemann, 1953), II, 308, p. 113.
† Op. cit., IV, 617, p. 293.

The ancients argued like this in the absence of any tangible evidence, whereas we have much clearer model concepts about the interaction of molecules in stimulant and receptor. Our concepts are based on measurement and experiment.

Olfactory sensitivity

The nose is a far more sensitive chemical detector than the tongue. A rather evil-smelling compound, mercaptane, is detected in incredibly small concentrations. A hundredth part of a milligram released into the air of a room 28 × 22 × 13 feet (230 cubic metres) is noticeable to an observer immediately on entering the room. It must be admitted that under these conditions a noseful of air still contains ten thousand million molecules of mercaptane! Assuming the nasal epithelium exposed to this mixture contains 50 million sensory cells, there would be 200 molecules of mercaptane available for each sensory cell. But this is only so if all the mercaptane molecules were brought in contact with the sensory surface of the nose, and such thoroughgoing distribution is, of course, highly unlikely. We may therefore be content with the assumption that each cell sensitive to mercaptane would have a chance under these conditions to receive one odoriferous molecule. With this we have again come to a point where, at the threshold of sensitivity, we are down to the mono-molecular level.

A few minutes after having entered the room the observer would no longer be able to smell the odour. We say he has become adapted to the scent. This is still the case with much higher concentrations of scent. I vividly remember a demonstration experiment designed to drive this home to a class of students. The lecturer had before the lecture released mercaptane into the air of the lecture room. Student after student showed signs of disgust on entering the room which smelt nauseatingly of rotten eggs. Soon, however, we all settled down and had forgotten all about it. Late-comers can always be expected, and the lecturer made good use of their invariable display of olfactory shock to remind us of the fact that the odour in the room was still as objectionable as before, but that we had become adapted to it.

At levels of just noticeable concentrations, or threshold concentrations as they are called, of substances like musk and the evil-smelling scatol, we deal with quantities which are no longer weighable on the finest balances and which would slip through any but the most sophisticated modern analytical techniques. The whole problem of olfactory sensitivity has recently been tackled by an ingenious technique which might be described as the technique of the 'model nose'. This technique rests on the assumption that the molecule of the odorant substance somehow pushes its way into the cell membrane of the receptor. We have seen how the theory of fundamental odours rests on a similar assumption. The variously-shaped molecules of odoriferous substances somehow fit into specific sites on the receptor membrane. Professor Davis and his colleagues in the Department of Chemical Engineering at Birmingham assume that the fit of the foreign molecule may not be absolutely perfect. In this case, small gaps may remain in the receptor membrane and this may cause a leak of potassium ions from the sensory cells. We have learnt how such a movement of ions across the membrane of excitable cells is the first step leading to the electric changes which finally give rise to the firing of frequency-coded impulses in the sensory nerves (see Introduction, p. 19). We are reminded again by this hypothesis of the possibility that in the retina the absorption of a light quantum by a molecule of visual pigment may lead to the appearance in part of the receptor membrane of a mono-molecular hole, through which potassium and sodium may exchange places between the inside and the outside of the receptor cell (Chapter 2, p. 45).

But what about Davis's 'model nose'? This, surprisingly, consists of an assembly of red blood corpuscles. These cells are affected by odoriferous substances. When brought in contact with them, the red blood cells begin to leak and the red pigment haemoglobin is released. The amount of haemoglobin lost per unit time can be accurately measured, and it was found that the rate of loss is characteristically different for different odoriferous substances. It was found that there is a close relationship between the power of a substance to weaken the cell membrane and its power to stimulate the nasal receptors. The haemolysing power of such a substance is therefore inversely proportional to its olfactory threshold concentration. This relationship can be put on a mathematical basis, and equations have been formulated with the aid of which the olfactory threshold of substances can be fairly accurately predicted after measurement of their haemolysing effect on red blood corpuscles.

The sense of smell in animals

It has been our habit when dealing with our own sense organs to look over our shoulder at some selected group of our fellow animals in order to see how they cope with similar situations. More often than not it was revealed that their sensory mechanisms surpass ours in one or the other aspect of function – be it in absolute sensitivity, in resolution, in range or in refinement of utilization of sensory information. Many of our fellow mammals score heavily on one or more of these counts. The olfactory prowess of dogs is notorious. They are more highly sensitive to most odoriferous substances, but they chiefly score by their ability to discriminate between different odours and by being able to pick a specific odour out of a mixture of many. This is how a dog recognizes the individual odour of its master against a background of many other odours, which may be much more highly concentrated. Police dogs are able to recognize the individual odour of the trainer's hand on pieces of wood which they have to retrieve, even if the wood was in loose contact with the hand for as short a time as one or two seconds, and despite the fact that the wood may have been heavily dosed with a strong scent, such as oil of cloves.

The appreciation of the odour of individual fellow animals plays, of course, an important part in mutual recognition and in territorial behaviour. A dog marks its own territory by deposition of urine. Every dog owner knows only too well the tedium of having to bear with one's dog's intensive and time-consuming olfactory inspection of the territory. This must give to the dog a vivid and unambiguous documentary account of what happened 'dog-wise' in its territory for hours before it started on the olfactory census of all comers, including, of course, intrusions by rivals or the presence of potential mates. If dogs had a true sense of gratitude, they would long have erected a monument to the human inventor of the lamp-post! Many mammals have special scent glands to advertise their presence in this way to friend and foe.

It is often said that birds do not pay much attention to scent, and an inspection of their nasal equipment shows that this is usually poor. There are exceptions. Some fish-eating marine birds, like petrels, have well-developed nasal conchs with a good expanse of sensory epithelium. There are also special valve-like structures designed to keep salt water away from the sensory cells when the bird dives under the surface for its prey. Ducks, too, have a better sense of smell than most birds. In an experiment in which food covered by 4 inches of snow was offered to ducks and hens, the ducks spotted the food immediately, whereas the hens remained oblivious of its presence. On the other hand, vultures which scavenge carrion that can only be described as 'extremely high' don't find it when it is out of sight. Hunters make use of this observation by covering their dead quarry with branches and foliage to keep vultures away.

Snakes can follow a spoor and turtles have been found to locate odoriferous food hidden in containers, ignoring similar containers filled with sand. When a snake has struck a prey the victim usually runs away and hides. The snake has no difficulty in retrieving it even in pitch darkness. In this it is guided by its sense of smell. We have also seen that some snakes are extremely sensitive to radiant heat (Chapter 4), and that they utilize this in the localization especially of warm-blooded prey. The fully aquatic newts among the Amphibia are known to orientate by smell, and are said to use traces of their own individual body odour for homing.

We have already seen that fish have an acute sense of taste with receptor organs distributed all over the body. They have noses, too, and these are peculiar in so far as there is no communication between the nose and the mouth cavity. The two receptor stations are therefore completely separate. A minnow can distinguish between the three odours cumarin, moschus, and scatol and it can be shown that they cease to notice their presence in the water when their use of the nasal organ is prevented by blocking the nose or by interruption of the nerve supply.

All this may be quite interesting, but, so far as the sense of smell is concerned, insects are the peers of all their fellow animals. In insects, too, one can distinguish between a sense of smell and a sense of taste, and it has been possible in quite a number of cases to identify the sense organs responsible for one or the other. On the whole, the organs of smell are found chiefly on the feelers. The organs of taste lie in and around the mouth and, strange to relate, on the feet. A housefly, for instance, can taste with its feet. On alighting on a source of food the contact between the food or a drinkable fluid and the sole of a foot makes a hungry or thirsty fly protrude its proboscis into it.

The receptor organs are sensory hairs with an interesting internal structure (Figure 35). They contain three to five sensory nerve cells, which each send a process into the cavity of the hollow hair. This cavity is subdivided into two channels.

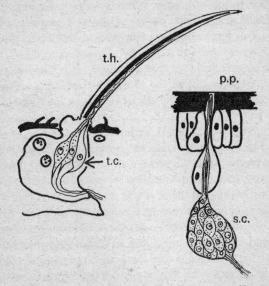

Figure 35. This shows a taste hair of a fly (t.h.), and an olfactory pore plate on the antenna of the honey bee (p.p.). One channel of the hollow taste hair is seen to carry the nerve processes from two of the three receptor cells. The third process ends at the joint of the hair and belongs to a tactile cell (t.c.). Apart from the tactile cell such taste hairs can contain up to five taste cells. The olfactory organ (p.p.) contains the processes from a large number of sensory cells (s.c.). They end in a pore of the chitinous cuticle of the feeler. (*Taste hair modified after Dethier.*)

One is apparently empty, the other contains all nerve processes except one which ends near the joint of the hair. This short process is a mechanoreceptor and responds to the bending of the hair on impact with an object. The other processes run right up to the tip of the hair and have been found to be separately sensitive to sugar, certain salts and organic substances, and to pure water. The presence of a receptor for pure water is interesting. We have already heard of similar receptor endings in backboned animals (p. 170). The feet of butterflies and moths are in the same way sensitive to chemical stimuli, to which the insects react by the unrolling of their long coiled-up proboscis.

It is fortunate that in insects the taste receptors and the feeding organ reacting to taste stimuli are found at two opposite ends of the body, so to speak. This makes it easy to test the range of taste and especially the threshold sensitivity to various substances. You have only to fasten a fly or butterfly to a holder, touch its feet with a solution of the experimental substance, and the delicately poised reaction of the proboscis shows you whether the stimulus has been effective. After you have given water in this way to a thirsty fly, and after it has drunk its fill, it will no longer protrude its proboscis on contact with water. However, if you now add some sugar to the water, renewed contact will at once make the insect protrude its proboscis again. A most amazing refinement of this technique, due to Professor Dethier and collaborators in the United States, made it possible to test single taste hairs in this way, and to observe and record the feeding reactions of the insect as well as the nerve impulses generated in the sensory nerves at the same time.

The sensitivity of insects to certain scents is legendary. A well-known case is the reaction of the male silk-moth to the odour liberated by the scent glands on the abdomen of the female. A female placed somewhere in the field under a hood made of wire gauze attracts the visit of males over incredible distances. The males of the silk-moth (*Actias selene*) were taken by train to a place two and a half miles away from a site where a female was exposed in this way. Forty per cent of the marked males found their way back to the female. In another experiment 26 per cent of the males returned over a distance of about seven miles. Naturally the direction of the wind must play an important role in such a feat of orientation towards a source of scent. Nevertheless, it is still not quite clear how the target is located, when the absolute quantities of the odoriferous substance in the air must be minute to start with, and when the gradient of increasing concentration is very slight, except in the immediate vicinity of the female. If one covers the female with a glass jar, males will not find it, even if they are released near the bait. However, a piece of paper, brought in contact with the opening of the female's scent gland and then exposed under a hood of gauze, will attract males as easily as a living female. If they have access to such a piece of scented paper, they will try to mate with it.

Insects which forage the nectar and pollen of flowering plants locate them not only by recognizing their shape and colour but they are also attracted to them by scent. A honey bee which has been trained to associate a certain scent with a rich yield of nectar will pick out a source which emits this scent from up to fifty different ones planted all around it. Parasitic insects which lay their eggs into the bodies of insect larvae are known to locate such larvae accurately even if they are hidden from touch or sight.

The receptors for odours are like the taste receptors – modified hollow hair organs (Figure 35). They differ from taste hairs by having generally many more sensory nerve cells associated with the hair process. This may mean that they possess specific receptors for a number of fundamental odours. In some cases the scent receptors lie in pits which are covered by a thin membrane. The feelers of the honey bee are covered with such so-called 'pore plates'. These are chiefly found on eight of the eleven end-joints of the feelers. Amputation of these leads to a loss of the sense of smell. However, if only seven joints are amputated, the insect can still distinguish a given scent from others.

Often it is impossible to make a distinction between taste and smell, especially in the lower backboneless animals. We speak in such cases of a general chemical sense. The importance of the chemical sense in the finding and recognition of friend and foe and mates, and in the finding and selection of food and drink and in orientation and territorial behaviour are only too obvious. Recently it has, however, become clear that minute adjustments of behaviour, especially between individual members of social or generally gregarious animals, depend often to a large extent on the liberation of chemical substances which produce reactions capable of coordination and guiding the behaviour of individuals. Many of these act by being taken up with the food. Others, however, are sensed by organs of the general chemical sense and produce their effect by influencing behaviour directly. In this case, minute amounts of substances can be effective over considerable distances.

Let us end the story of the chemical sense with an example which, at first sight, seems to be far removed from the culinary pleasures of a Christmas dinner that triggered off our study of it at the beginning of this chapter.

It is a well-known fact that the spawning of a number of sessile or slightly mobile marine organisms, during which both eggs and sperm are liberated into the water by females and males, happens simultaneously over long stretches of sea shore. This is just as well, because, in the interests of successful fertilization, the sexual products must unite soon after liberation. What guarantees the correct timing of spawning? It has been thought that the moon or the state of the tides has something to do with this. However, it is believed that the immediate stimulus that triggers off the release of eggs and sperm is a chemical substance liberated in minute quantities from the body of mature individuals. This acts as a chemical stimulus and brings about the simultaneous spawning reaction in hundreds of thousand individuals.

THE SENSORY CENTRES

The visual pathway

ON a number of occasions we have mentioned that sensory information in the form of electric pulses flows along nervous pathways towards the central nervous system. The terminus may be in the spinal cord or in the brain, and there may be a varying number of intermediate stations at which the coded information has to be transferred from the processes of one neuron to those of another. One speaks of first-, second-, third-order neurons, and so on. In the case of our eye the first-order neurons would be the bipolar nerve cells in the retina which furnish the link between rods and cones and the second-order ganglion cells. These still lie in the retina forming its outer nuclear layer (see Figure 9).

The long processes of the second-order retinal ganglion cells enter the brain proper. Their distribution over the right and left halves of the brain is interesting. The fibres from the outer or lateral halves of the retina of the right and left eye run straight to the right and left halves of the brain respectively. The fibres from the inner (nasal) halves of the eyes cross over to the opposite side of the brain. Thus each half of the brain receives fibres from both eyes.

The first relay station in the brain is the geniculate body. From there third-order neurons carry visual information to the visual cortex at the back of the brain just above the back of our neck either directly or via an intermediate relay station in the thalamus (Figure 36). There are branch lines to other parts of the brain. They are of little interest to us.

What happens in the cortex? The response of the neurons in the cortex is very complex. The cortex is arranged in layers of neurons and they become excited one after another. The final result is the appearance of slow electric waves at the surface of the cortex. There is also a return relay of excitation from the cortex to the lower centres of the brain. In fact, what happens is so complicated that a modern high-speed computer would probably not be able to disentangle it, even if we

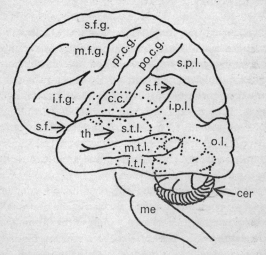

Figure 36. This is a diagrammatic representation of the fissures, gyri, and lobes of the human cortex. In addition, the approximate positions of inner parts of the brain, such as the corpus callosum (c.c.), the thalamus (th), and the cerebellum (cer), are indicated. The localizations of sensory end-stations in the various parts of the cortex are given in the text. Not by any means all of these are indicated here. A number of them lie hidden within the tissue of the brain.

s.f.g.	superior frontal gyrus	s.f.	sylvian fissure
m.f.g.	median frontal gyrus	s.t.l.	superior temporal lobe
i.f.g.	inferior frontal gyrus	m.t.l.	median temporal lobe
pr.c.g.	pre-central gyrus	i.t.l.	inferior temporal lobe
po.c.g.	post-central gyrus	o.l.	occipital lobe
s.p.l.	superior parietal lobe	me	medulla
i.p.l.	inferior parietal lobe		

had all the data necessary to feed into it. Let this be the concern of the neurophysiologist. But what about vision? Have we any idea how the events in the cortex are related to the image we see? The answer is no. We shall discuss this a little more thoroughly in Chapter 11.

The olfactory pathway

We have started our study of the connexion between sense organs and brain with the eye and the optic or second brain nerve. The first nerve to the brain comes from the nose. We have already followed the path of the olfactory nerve fibres from the receptor layer in the nose to their junction with the processes of pyramidal cells in the olfactory bulb. These junctions are assembled in well-circumscribed, separate, and densely packed skeins of fibres known as glomeruli (Figure 33). The glomeruli are roughly spherical and appear to be sorting stations. It may well be that their separateness has something to do with the separate analysis of different fundamental odours. Two possibilities exist. Either each glomerulus (there are 2,000 glomeruli in an olfactory bulb of the rabbit and each receives about 25,000 nerve fibres) receives information from receptors specifically sensitive to one or the other fundamental odour; or, alternatively, the glomeruli receive messages at random from all types of receptors and the sorting is done by the 24 mitral cells which synapse with the 25,000 olfactory fibres terminating in each glomerulus.

There is some important experimental evidence which points towards the first of these alternatives as the more likely one. It comes from fairly recent work of Lord Adrian, who recorded the electric activity of the olfactory bulb of the cat and found that mitral cells can be subdivided into at least four or five different kinds, which have different sensitivities to different groups of odours. Such mitral cells may possibly have been connected to specific glomeruli, and this would be in agreement with the earlier discovery by Lord Adrian that high sensitivity to specific odours is localized in certain regions of the olfactory centre. This fact, too, would speak against a complete scrambling of connexions in the glomeruli as supported in the second alternative hypothesis.

The long processes of the mitral cells run from the olfactory bulb along the olfactory tract to a specific area of the cortex known as the pre-piriform cortex. Although the structure of this part of the cortex is simpler than that of the visual one, we are as yet far from being able to understand the basis for the final discrimination between odours – and, of course, the origin of olfactory sensation is as obscure as in all other sensory fields.

The gustatory pathway

We found that the information from the taste buds of the tongue reaches the brain via the seventh and ninth nerves to the hindmost part of the brain, the medulla oblongata. Here lie ganglion cells from which responses to stimulation of the tongue by taste substances can be recorded. There is a pathway from here to the cortex which terminates perhaps among other places in what is known as the post-central gyrus. This lies on the lateral side of the brain below the temple (Figure 36).

Taste sensations can be evoked in patients on electrical stimulation of this area of the brain. This can be done in a conscious patient during an operation on the brain. The brain itself is not pain sensitive, and all the patient reports in such a case are conscious taste sensations. With this experiment we have stumbled on a most important fact. We have been wondering how electric signals from sense organs can on their arrival at one or the other brain terminus 'give rise' to conscious sensations. We now see that electric stimulation experimentally applied to parts of such a cortical end-station is similarly accompanied by conscious sensory experience, the nature of which depends entirely on the specific region of the stimulated cortex. There are parts of the cortex situated not very far from the area just mentioned whose electric stimulation gives rise in the patient to fleeting memories of past events in his life. The memories are clear enough to be accurately described by the conscious patient. All this goes to show that we cannot be fundamentally wrong in attributing to the cortex of the brain an outstandingly important role in the elaboration of conscious experience. Damage to cortical areas can in fact lead to a permanent loss of sensitivity to taste and tactile stimuli. Taste and touch are here as elsewhere closely associated.

The tactile pathways

Tactile sense endings together with those sensitive to temperature and painful stimuli are widely distributed all over the body. The nervous pathways from the body surface to the central nervous system are correspondingly complex and it would not be very useful here to follow them in detail. Obviously signals of such widespread origin must travel to the central nervous system along every available pathway, directly from the face to the brain via the large fifth and seventh brain nerves and, for instance, from the organs of respiration, whence mechanical and chemical stimuli are relayed through the tenth nerve or vagus. All other pathways are routed through the numerous spinal nerves with a first relay station in the dorsal-root ganglion of the spinal cord. From there long columns of relaying neurons and fibres hand on tactile, thermal, and pain information upwards to the thalamus, one of the most important relay stations of the brain. From the thalamus they ultimately radiate on to the so-called post-central sensory gyrus Figure 36).

The kinesthetic pathways

In this connexion it is as well to remember that the kinesthetic part of the mechanical sense (Chapter 6, p. 104) with its sense-endings in and around the joints of our limbs is closely allied to all this and uses the same pathways right up to the cortex. In contrast to this it seems that the information from the stretch receptors in the muscles is poorly represented in the cortex. This fits in well with the fact that the reflex mechanisms triggered off by stretch receptors are not accessible to conscious control and that we are not aware of them (Chapter 6, pp. 102, 103). We have to look for the central end-stations of these receptors in the cerebellum, where they are closely associated with the inflow of information from the sense endings in the semicircular canals and otolith organs of the inner ear. Their function, too, is not directly accessible to conscious introspection unless the sense organs are over-stimulated. Then they can trigger off the unpleasant experiences connected with vertigo and nausea (Chapter 7, p. 128).

The labyrinthine pathways

The pathway between the ear labyrinth and the cerebellum lies along the eighth brain nerve via the ganglionic nucleus of Deiters to the base of the cerebellum and from there to the cerebellar cortex. As the cerebellum also receives offshoots from the tactile and kinesthetic pathways it is the ideal relay station governing the control of posture and movement. From it emanate coordinating commands to the postural and loco-motory body musculature.

The pathway from the cochlea of the ear to the brain is quite different. It will be remembered that the first-order ganglion cells lie close to the cochlea in the spiral ganglion which winds around the central column of the cochlear coil. They send their long processes into the acoustic portion of the eighth nerve. As in the case of the visual pathway there are quite a number of relay stations in various parts of the brain, which are of little interest to us. On following the more direct pathway to the cortical terminus connected with conscious sound perception the long fibres from the cochlear nucleus relay in parts of the brain known as inferior and superior colliculus and the medial geniculate body. We have heard of the geniculate body before, as the seat of the first relay station along the optical pathway. From there the acoustic information is relayed both to the cerebellum and to the cortex.

The acoustic end-stations

The acoustic area of the cortex lies in the temporal lobe of the brain (Figure 36), both on its outer surface and buried in the deep fold of the sylvian fissure. The auditory cortex is many-layered and exceptionally rich in cells and fibres. It is sub-divided into a sensory area and 'psychic' area. Sensation of sound is anchored in the sensory area, whereas appreciation of music and a proper understanding of sounds, especially those of speech, is anchored in the 'psychic' area. It was thought for a time that the cells in the acoustic cortex were arranged in such a way as to mirror the arrangement of the sensory cells along the organ of Corti in the cochlea. One spoke of an accurate topographic projection. In this case it ought to be possible to find separate end-stations for sounds of low and high pitch. However, it appears from more recent experiments that the separations may not be quite so accurate as all that, and thus cortical cells responding to low-, medium-, and high-pitched sounds can pretty well be found closely side by side.

Our rapid exploration of the pathways leading from sense organs to their final relay station in the central nervous system is over. However, there is one important fact which cannot be emphasized too strongly. The cortex is not only a receiving station for sensory information. Quite a lot of this information is redistributed from the cortex back to other parts of the brain. Also of great importance is the fact that the central nervous system sends a constant stream of messages to the sense organs themselves. These may be designed to adjust the sensitivity and receptive range of a given sense organ to the general state of external stimulation. One is just beginning to pay proper attention to these so-called centrifugal pathways.

Pain

One more vital matter remains to be dealt with. It will be recalled that our account of the 'sense of pain' in Chapter 5 (p. 99) was very scanty indeed. We were left under the impression that pain can either be due to the overstimulation of any given sense organ and that, besides this, there exist special nerve endings, often of small diameter, which are specifically stimulated by potentially destructive agencies. This is more or less what could usefully be considered when dealing with the skin as a sense organ. However, pain is a commanding and all-powerful sensation which, as has been mentioned, can even survive the disappearance of the initial source, as in the case of phantom pain. We must therefore assume that the central nervous system plays an overridingly important part in the elaboration of pain and suffering.

We all know only too well that the most excruciating pain, apart from toothache, comes from visceral organs and muscles and joints. Visceral pain is relayed via the tenth nerve and also along the complex pathways of the so-called sympathetic nervous system. The role played by the sympathetic nervous system in the processing and distribution of signals giving rise to painful sensations is the object of a lot of detailed neurological research. It is becoming increasingly clear that most parts of the so-called autonomous or involuntary nervous system, consisting of the sympathetic ganglia and nerves, and of the parasympathetic system, associated partly with the vagus nerve, carry such signals. All these are finally relayed to the brain. There is hardly a brain centre outside the reach of pain pathways. Among them the thalamus seems to play an important part. The cortical terminus appears to be located in the neighbourhood of the pre- and post-central gyri of the brain (Figure 36). However, it would be unwise to assume that we have at present enough information to map out the centres, singly or in combination, which contribute to the experience of pain.

Many valuable data are collected by surgeons in their often desperate attempts to stop overpowering pain by sectioning of this or that nervous pathway connected with diseased organs. This is a slow and haphazard process, and our relative lack of information is due to the fact that a suffering man is the only reliable source of information on pain. Alas, this information can be very misleading. A patient suffering from severe phantom pain can only point in the direction of a long-lost limb to indicate its origin, and the intriguing phenomena of referred pain can add to the confusion. Referred pain often arises from impulses in one deep-seated organ, but is localized by the sufferer somewhere at the surface of the body. A lot of backache and many types of headache fall within this category of pain. One explanation why we should think we have a pain somewhere in the skin, when the source of the trouble may be the appendix, the heart, or the womb, is that pathways from these organs have no direct connexion with the brain but relay on to the same neuron as pain fibres from the skin. Consequently, a stream of impulses from the diseased organ is interpreted by the sufferer as coming from the areas of skin connected with this relay station. Physicians use maps of the body surface showing certain common targets of referred pain, and a tenderness of the skin in a certain place can be a useful guide to the real spot of trouble.

The phenomenon of pain has given rise to a lot of biological, philosophical, and religious controversy. What, people have asked, is the meaning of pain? Doubtlessly its survival value lies in its importance as a warning to the organism that all is not well with the machinery of its body. Dangerous over-activity is restrained by it, and attention is directed to the ailing part. A dog will be induced by pain to lick a sore paw and thus to apply antiseptic saliva to the wound, and we are sent by it to our doctor's surgery – often in good time for successful treatment, sometimes unfortunately too late. The times have passed when pain was considered a punishment inflicted by a vengeful god, an idea largely responsible for all the religious doubt and perplexity that has centred on the contradiction be-tween an all-merciful deity and the torments of pain. To end this account of pain on a lighter note: let us assume the atti-tude that, apart from its purely biological function, the occas-ional intrusion of pain into our lives can give us a heightened appreciation and enjoyment of good health!

THE PHILOSOPHY OF
SENSATION

Our journey around the world of sense has revealed to us an astonishing degree of similarity in difference. The stimuli may be very different. The organs whose job it is to mediate between the stimulus in its original physico-chemical form and the receptor structures which transduce the various stimuli into a coded nervous message may be very complex. Yet the nervous message itself is likely to consist monotonously of electric pulses. Their frequency in many cases conveys information about the intensity of the stimulus only. Information about the nature or modality of the stimulus is in most cases derived from the whereabouts of the final end-station in the central nervous system. To this the coded message is routed along the nervous pathways connecting sensory receptors with the central computers. We have surveyed these end-stations in the human brain and have found that the arrival of the coded impulse trains results in most cases in electric phenomena that can be recorded, usually in the form of relatively slow waves of changing potential from these various areas of the brain. Our measuring instruments respond to such events by movements of pointers or electron beams. Their responses are recorded on paper by pens attached to the pointers or on film exposed to the phosphorescent face of oscillograph tubes. On these the electron beams moving in the rhythm of the electric waves and pulses write a fleeting image of the electric signals after they have been amplified a million times by complex radio circuits. It then appears that the raw material from which our experience of the world around us is pieced together consists of nothing but electric pulses commuting from one part of our nervous system to another.

But what we experience are not electrical pulses but light, shape, colour, or noise, the sound of a voice or chords of music, the hardness of steel or the moist softness of a woman's lips, the delicious freshness of a ripe fruit picked from a tree by the deftly coordinated action of eye, arm, and hand. By adding the complex lens system of microscope or telescope to the lens of our eye we make ourselves see the microcosm inhabited by microbes, the architecture of the living body and the crystal structure of minerals and metals. We see the stars and galaxies in the vastness of the universe around us. We can by means of sensitive instruments 'feel' and record the slightest tremors of our earth, even the beat of the ocean waves on the shores of our continents. We can make visible on dials and screens the pulses of radioactive and cosmic radiations and make audible through loudspeakers the mysterious noises emitted by dark radiostars collected by the gigantic bowls of radio-telescopes. We can 'sense' the heat of stars and the speed of their headlong movement away from us in an ever-expanding universe. Whatever we observe in science, even if we use complex computers and the analysing power of our brains, all of it ultimately reaches our conscious understanding through one or the other sensory channel, in which all of it is layed out in intricate patterns of electric change.

What is the relationship between these electric patterns in our nervous system and the world around us? This is an age-old question. It has exercised the minds of generations of thinkers. When the ancient Greek nature philosophers, foremost among them Leucippus and Democritus (fifth century B.C.), gradually realized that the world as conveyed to them through their senses was a world of appearances, they tried to imagine what it was really like. They came to the conclusion that it was made up of atoms and space. The atoms had mass, shape, and movement, but apart from this no sensible qualities. Objects of sense were nothing but associations of such atoms into complex patterns.

The impact of these patterns of moving atoms on similar patterns making up our body set in motion our organs of sense. In this way they created an 'impression' of the lifeless and living objects around us. All this was summarized at the end of the pre-Christian era by Lucretius, whose great poem *De rerum natura* ('On the Nature of Things'), is available in good English translations and makes astonishingly topical reading.

European man's interest in the nature of his world lay dormant for sixteen centuries. When it awoke again in the glorious seventeenth century modern science was born. Naturally, the question of the relationship between the objects in the world around us and with our own conscious experience of them was reopened by the thinkers of that age. Thomas Hobbes (1588–1679) deals with the Nature of Man in the first part of his book *Leviathan*. In its first chapter devoted to 'Sense' we find the famous statement: 'There is no conception in Man's mind which hath not at first totally or in parts, been begotten upon the organs of sense.' It may be of interest to quote one paragraph from this chapter in full. *

The cause of Sense, is the Externall Body, or Object, which presseth the organ proper to each Sense either immediatly, as in the Taste and Touch; or mediately, as in Seeing, Hearing, and Smelling: which pressure, by the mediation of Nerves, and other strings, and membranes of the body, continued inwards to the Brain, and Heart, causeth there a resistance, or counter pressure, or endeavour of the Heart, to deliver it self: which endeavour because Outward, seemeth to be some matter without. And this seeming, or fancy, is that which men call Sense; and con-

* From the edition prepared by A. D. Lindsay (Everyman's Library, 691, Aldine Press, 1914).

sisteth, as to the Eye, in a Light, or Colour figured; To the Eare, in a Sound; To the Nostrill, in an Odour; To the tongue and Palat, in a Savour; And to the rest of the body, in Heat, Cold, Hardnesse, Softnesse, and such other qualities, as we discern by Feeling. All which qualities called Sensible, are in the object that causeth them, but so many several motions of the matter, by which it presseth our organs diversely. Neither in us that are pressed, are they any thing else, but divers motions; (for motion, produceth nothing but motion). But their apparence to us is Fancy, the same waking, that dreaming. And as pressing, rubbing, or striking the Eye, makes us fancy a light; and pressing the Eare, produceth a dinne; so do the bodies also we see, or hear, produce the same by their strong, though unobserved actions. For if those Colours, and Sounds, were in the Bodies, or Objects that cause them, they could not bee severed from them, as by glasses, and in Ecchoes by reflection, wee see they are; where we know the thing we see, is in one place; the apparence, in another. And though at some certain distance, the reall, and very object seem invested with the fancy it begets in us; Yet still the object is one thing, the image or fancy is another. So that Sense in all cases, is nothing els but original fancy, caused (as I have said) by the pressure, that is, by the motion, of externall things upon our Eyes, Eares, and other organs thereunto ordained.

This revealing passage shows how clearly Hobbes had made himself realize that 'quality' in an object is in fact the product of what he calls Fancy. Of course, Hobbes was aware of the teaching of the Greek philosophers and of the trends of thought of his time. For our purpose it may be sufficient to follow what formulation was given to these insights by the great empiricist John Locke. Locke in his *Essay Concerning Human Understanding*, published first in 1690, considered that in our conscious mind we have several types of 'ideas' which make up the sum total of our knowledge. A new-born baby's mind was likened by Locke to a white sheet of paper devoid of any ideas.

Experience from earliest infancy onward furnishes man with ideas of which the first are derived from sensation. These are the ideas like yellow, white, heat, cold, soft, hard, bitter, or sweet. In the course of his inquiry into the sources of human understanding Locke defines whatever has the power to produce an idea of sensation in our mind as the quality of an object. Among the qualities he distinguishes first those utterly inseparable from a body. They are solidity, extension, figure, motion, rest, and number. He calls them primary qualities. They reside in the objects which make up the world. Besides these there are what he calls secondary qualities. They, according to Locke, do not reside as such in the objects, but are best described as the power of the objects to produce various sensations in us through the operation of combinations of their primary qualities. These secondary qualities produce the ideas of sensation such as colour, sounds, tastes, and others. Locke was, of course, puzzled how objects can act on our senses over a distance and here he did not succeed in going far beyond the imagery of the ancient philosophers: he assumed with them that corporeal replicas of objects must emanate from them, and by impact with our organs of sense impart their configuration and motion on them. Thus they create in our mind the primary and secondary ideas concerning the world around us. It would lead us too far if we wanted to follow on from Locke in a historical survey of the development of these ideas in the various philosophical schools, Anglo-Saxon, French, German, or other.

We listen to a philosophical discussion

It might be interesting to listen in to a discussion as it might take place today among any mixed group made up of scientists, philosophers, and educated laymen, a discussion which might be said to aim at a clarification of our views on the problem of the relationship between the sensory process and our conscious experience of the world. Let us assume our group consists of a physicist, a biologist, a philosopher, and an artist. In the chair we find as so often nowdays a person whose job on such occasions is to adopt the attitude of the man in the street, who approaches all questions from the point of view of naïve common sense.

CHAIRMAN: The basis of our discussion on the relationship between sensory perception and conscious experience of the world is a book on 'Sense' in which the author describes the mechanism of sensory reception in man and other animals. As you will have noticed this description follows the various physical or chemical stimuli to which the animal organism is exposed on their way from the environment to the sense organ and from there along the sensory nerves to the brain or other parts of the central nervous system. Their pathway ends in the highest brain centres. These are occasionally compared with computing stations in which the information coded in terms of electrical nerve impulses is sorted out and somehow forms the basis for the conscious experience evoked by the various stimuli. I hope I have summed this up correctly.

BIOLOGIST: Perfectly.

CHAIRMAN: Well, then, here goes. May I call on our philosopher first?

PHILOSOPHER: Before we start, I should like to point out that I am taking part in this discussion not as a representative of a special school of philosophy. Of course, I belong to one, but I shall try to be as neutral as possible and argue on the basis of widely accepted philosophical fundamentals only. Now the first thing we must do is to agree on what we mean by 'relationship between sensory stimulus and conscious experience'. I suggest, Mr Chairman, that I tackle the term 'relationship' first.

CHAIRMAN: Go ahead.

PHILOSOPHER: The best approach, I feel, would be if we used this term to mean a strict 'cause-and-effect relationship'. The stimulus is the cause and the conscious experience is the effect. So that our discussion is not confined to a vacuum, it might be useful to have a definite combination of stimuli in mind. As a professional philosopher I should, of course, now suggest that we imagine a table as the source of these stimuli. However, in the presence of an artist I relent and suggest a red rose instead.

We shall investigate how our conscious experience of its graceful shape, flaming colour, and sweet scent, as well as of its thorniness are related to the object itself. I should therefore like to ask whether there is a way to describe the rose in purely physical terms, as this might give us the first link in our causal chain.

BIOLOGIST: Mr Chairman, may I intervene here by asking whether I am talking sense if I say that there would not be such a thing as a physical object in a universe in which there is no centre for conscious experience, such as a thinking animal. I should like to suggest, therefore, that we agree first on what is meant by conscious experience.

CHAIRMAN: I should have thought that this is not at all a difficult thing to agree on. Haven't we all got consciousness? So we ought to know what it is like. A pity we haven't a red scented rose here. If we had, our problem would be solved. We should just say: this is conscious experience of a rose.

ARTIST: I don't think it is as simple as all this, because I am sure that my experience of the rose would probably differ from any of yours. You see, I should probably want to paint it, and being a modern artist the picture in my mind may have very little to do with your rose.

CHAIRMAN: But it would still be caused by the rose would it

not? And, therefore, we should still have our relation between object and experience?

ARTIST: I should not be so sure. A lot of my experience might
be quite unconnected with the actual rose.

BIOLOGIST: I accept the argument that we all know what conscious experience feels like in ourselves. But are we so sure
about it in other people; for instance, as we have just seen in
the case of an artist? Much more difficult is the question
what the conscious experience of our fellow animals might
be like. Here I should like to repeat what I tell my students
in this context. I put it to them that we have no scientifically
defensible reason to deny some sort of consciousness to any
animal with a reasonably well-developed nervous system.
Apart from this, we can only *guess* what other conscious-
nesses are like.

PHYSICIST: Let me say first of all that the question of the
nature of conscious experience has now been aired before I
could make an attempt to describe our rose in purely physical
terms. Let me ask what biologists think the consciousness
of a dog or cat is like?

BIOLOGIST: I have pondered this question a lot and have
come to the conclusion that the consciousness of an animal
may consist entirely of images in terms of the animal's
dominant senses. However, these images are nameless. Animals have no abstract concepts. Unlike man, they have no
symbolic vocabulary. Their memories must therefore be
compounded of combinations of wordless sensory 'images'.
In the case of our rose, of course, we have it from the book
that whatever its image in the consciousness of our dog may
be – provided he pays attention to it – it is not red. Otherwise it may well be similar to our own with a great emphasis
on the scent, of course. If he were made to retrieve the rose,
the thorns would naturally loom large in the dog's 'mind'
and may well form the chief item of association.

CHAIRMAN: I see some eyebrows go up.

PHILOSOPHER: Yes, aren't we jumping to conclusions in alleging the absence of concepts of abstract 'ideas' in the dog's conscious make-up? Just because we cannot possibly imagine what they would be like in the absence of a human type language, ought we therefore to deny their existence?

CHAIRMAN: I don't quite know whether I understand what you mean, but I have a feeling you are introducing a red herring. I have no difficulty in granting some sort of conscious experience to the dog. Frankly, I had taken it for granted. I want, however, to return to the contention that there would not be a rose if there was nobody to experience it. I should have thought the rose would still be there just the same. Now, I am sure, this is a matter on which a physicist must have strong opinions.

PHYSICIST: I think it is rather futile to speculate how things would be in a non-experiencing universe. I feel philosophers would agree with me that such a question is meaningless, because it is not open to disproof or to verification.

PHILOSOPHER: You are adopting the positivist attitude, that metaphysics is meaningless and therefore a waste of time and effort. However, don't forget that such questions have been asked from time immemorial and that they will be asked as long as animals capable of reflection exist in the universe. The question as such is a 'natural phenomenon' and as such deserves attention.

PHYSICIST: All right. But let me say that I should be unhappy as a person and ineffectual as a practising scientist if I were not allowed to assume that the rose is real. Of course, its colour and scent are, as John Locke pointed out, secondary qualities, which arise from the causal interaction between its physical properties (or powers) and the organism. Let us then look at these physical properties and forget for the moment that they, too, have become known to us through our senses and that the names we give them are concepts that have been conceived in human minds. In fact, our book has stated them all quite clearly, and dispassionately.

I think it is in a way rather unfortunate that we have chosen a rose. A rose is a living thing and much of its composition is due to the interplay of very complex happenings. I should have preferred to discuss a crystal of quartz, for instance. This would be much simpler.

BIOLOGIST: I don't think it makes any difference. Let us then assume that there exists in the place where we believe we see our rose the assembly of molecules each composed of a few or many atoms. The way in which they are arranged is not unique. There are, in fact, many such assemblies of matter closely alike, and they are connected with one another by events which we would call the processes of growth, development, reproduction, and heredity. There were generations of such assemblies before. There exist many of them now, and there will be as many or more of them in the future. They belong to a certain species of object. The specific and, as such, inherited characters ensure that the molecules making up the object occupy space in a characteristic way, which we recognize as the typical shape of the object. There is its stem complete with leaves and thorns and there is its flower-head adorned with coloured petals.

PHYSICIST: All right, then. Let me take over the argument here. Our rose is exposed to a continuous bombardment by electromagnetic waves or energy quanta derived either from the far-distant sun or from the glowing filament of a light bulb. Some of these waves are absorbed by the molecules making up the body of the rose. Others are bounced back or reflected. The wavelengths of the reflected waves depend on the chemical composition of the various parts of the plant, and this is different in stem and flower. So it comes about that the stem reflects radiation of one wavelength and the petals of the flower that of another. These reflected wave-lengths reach the assembly of molecules from which our eye is made up and are – as the book tells us – absorbed in the cells of the retina. There they produce certain effects, which have also been described in the book and which I am not competent to discuss. Similarly, some of the substances making up the rose are volatile, that is to say they leave the rose and are carried by the air into our nose. There they interact with certain cells producing effects quite similar to those produced by electromagnetic waves in the retina of the eye. Why certain molecules reflect this or that part of the electromagnetic spectrum, and why certain substances stay put and others evaporate at room temperature are questions belonging to the field of physico-chemistry.

CHAIRMAN: It seems to me now that we can deal with a rose as easily as with a quartz crystal after all. There is even the advantage in that the rose has striking colours and scent. This widens the field, doesn't it? By the way, am I to understand that the rose itself is not green and red, but only reflects green and red light?

PHILOSOPHER: If you say the rose is not green and red, you must not say that the light is green or red either. Greenness and redness are phenomena of living experience.

CHAIRMAN: This seems rather a dreary kind of universe in which there are only aggregations of atoms and radiation.

PHILOSOPHER: Nevertheless, this is not only the kind of universe postulated on the basis of the triumphs of modern experimental science but also the universe as described ages ago by the ancient nature philosophers on the basis of rational thought unsupported by measurement and analysis, nay, even strongly contradicted by the evidence of their senses.

ARTIST: However, it is a comforting thought that we need not jump to the conclusion that our world is a dull mechanical jumble of particles and waves only. I claim it does contain the whole splendour of light, colour, scent, and so on, and that we find them inside rather than outside us.

CHAIRMAN: Thank you a thousand times. I had for an anxious moment lost all joy in the world when I was told that sensible objects lack all the very qualities we enjoy so much in them.

BIOLOGIST: We know how the organism responds to the physical properties of the world around it by setting up streams of electric pulses. We know how these coded signals travel to the outposts of the central nervous system, and how they are transformed there into other kinds of electric waves. We also know that precisely similar electric events can be measured in the nervous system of all animals. We have also been shown convincing evidence in the book that animals appear to differentiate in their responses between different types of stimuli in much the same way as we do on the basis of our conscious experience of different qualities of light, colour, taste, or scent. We have been asked to believe that animals see colour and distinguish between sounds of different pitch. You have, I hope, accepted the reasonableness of my statement that we have no cause to deny conscious experience to many of our fellow animals. Yet I ask, what do we know about the origin of conscious experience? The answer is: nothing. What is more, it may be suggested that this question is fundamentally unanswerable. Redness is a private experience. Although it may be triggered off by the arrival of nervous impulses in a highly specific part of our brain, there does not seem to be a physical connexion between it and the nerve impulse. I mean a connexion of the kind we find in cause-and-effect relationships, say between the heating of a block of ice and its melting into a corresponding volume of water.

PHYSICIST: Yes, you are putting your finger on the spot. We

have so far no reason to believe that conscious experience is a form of energy, and we cannot say in fact that nerve impulses are converted into experience in the same way as heat is converted into motion in a steam engine. The process seems to be irreversible, and outside what we would call the laws of thermodynamics.

PHILOSOPHER: Yes, Mr Chairman, what Hobbes called the Fancy and what we call the Mind is inseparably at one with the substance of the universe. It is closely interwoven with it. It is also well-nigh impossible to unravel the relationship between it and the rest of the living organism in which it operates. The seventeenth-century French philosopher René Descartes was wrong in distinguishing between mind-less animals, which he described as mere mechanisms, and man, in whom he saw the mechanism of the body accompanied by and interacting with a potentially independent mind – animals, too, could claim possession of it. And so I feel the best way of looking at the relation between the physical world and the world of conscious experience is to consider them as a unitary whole which is capable of conscious experience of its own self wherever its material or energetic make-up reaches the high degree of complexity of animal organization.

CHAIRMAN: I believe that with this summing-up we have reached a point at which it may be appropriate to end our discussion. I wish we had a scented red rose on the table, to reassure us that all is well. In its absence I have to take your word for it. Thank you.

A postscript on extrasensory perception

After a public lecture to radio, television, or extramural audiences on a topic connected with sensory function the lecturer finds among letters he receives or among the questions asked in discussion almost invariably one or more questions on extrasensory perception or E.S.P.

Of course, it would be easy to evade the issue by answering that the subject of the lecture having been sensory perception the question does not arise. This would not be a very helpful answer. It might even be considered evasive and rude. Interest is very strong in what are sometimes called 'para-normal' phenomena, not only because they savour of spooks and goose-flesh but quite genuinely because we have become somewhat accustomed to consider almost nothing as impossible. Literally hundreds of orbiting objects of the most fantastic shapes and scientific uses whirl about in outer space and this is taken for granted only a few years after the first sputnik was set racing around the globe. An instantaneous transatlantic transmission of an important event by Telstar is expected as a matter of course, and, if the picture disappears for a few minutes or jiggers about, we are liable to say 'somebody has bungled this one!'

So the value of the word 'impossible' has been depreciated enormously on the stock exchange of our thinking. We have learnt by experience throughout the three centuries of scientific adventure that yesterday's miracles are today's commonplace. Why not, then, expect that sooner or later all those sceptics who at present still refuse to believe in E.S.P. will have to admit that information can and does flow between individuals of our species when they are not in sensory contact with one another. This means that a man in Birmingham may, in fact, at a given moment become aware of events that happen in London, without being linked with the event by any of the known means of telecommunication, such as telegraph, telephone, radio, or television. And yet, no light rays, no sound waves, no quanta of energy, or atoms and molecules of matter can be shown to have traversed the 100-mile gap and to have found entry into his living room or bedroom through closed doors.

Such feats of extrasensory perception have been reported in all earnestness, and the name telepathy springs to our mind when we hear of them. Telepathy means feeling or sensing over a distance, and there are books full of alleged cases of that kind. Of course, the question a serious investigator has to ask himself first and foremost is whether the stories reported are fact, and whether they were documented at the moment of happening in such a manner as to leave no reasonable doubt concerning their authenticity. If so, he has to ask whether there was really no alternative explanation in terms of more orthodox means of communication between the communicating partners. Only then would it be worth while to bring the whole scientific machinery to bear on a search for a vehicle for such communication.

I don't know whether there is, in fact, a single sufficiently documented case to go on with. The famous experiments with cards in which one party is reported to have stated which card a remote partner was turning over from a randomly assorted pack have, in some cases, yielded results that suggest E.S.P. However, these results are based on elaborate statistics and there are many, among them I myself, who think it might be worth while to investigate the validity of the statistical techniques used before accepting that there has been a genuine transfer of information between the partners, in which none of the known sensory channels were involved. This is where I should like to leave this matter. Often such phenomena are called 'para-normal' – beyond the boundaries of the normal. The late J. B. S. Haldane once pointed out, when chairing a meeting of a professional Biological Society, at which the most recently available reports on such experiments were discussed, that, if such communication could be convincingly and repeatably demonstrated, it would cease to be para-normal. Scientists would then be only too prepared to attempt to find the mechanism.

ARTICLES AND BOOKS FOR
FURTHER READING

ADRIAN, E. D. *The Physical Background of Perception*. The Clarendon Press, Oxford, 1947.

AMOORE, J. E., JOHNSTON, J. W., Jr, and RUBIN, M. 'The stereochemical theory of odor'. *Scientic American* **20**, 44–9, February 1964.

BARKER, D. (ed.). *Symposium on Muscle Receptors*. Hong Kong University Press, 1962.

BEATTY, R. T. *Hearing in Man and Animals*. G. Bell & Sons, London, 1932.

BELL, G. H., DAVIDSON, J. N., and SCARBOROUGH, H. *Textbook of Physiology and Biochemistry*. E. S. Livingstone, Edinburgh, 1950.

BROWN, M. (ed.). *The Physiology of Fishes*, Volume 2. Academic Press, New York, 1957.

BULLOCK, T. H., and DIECKE, F. P. J. 'Properties of an infra-red receptor'. *J. Physiol.* **134**, 47–87, Cambridge University Press, 1956.

CARTHY, J. D. *Animal Navigation*. George Allen & Unwin, London, 1956.

DAVSON, H. *The Physiology of the Eye*. J. & A. Churchill, London, 1963.

FANTZ, R. L. *Scientific American* **204**, 66–72, May 1961.

FRAENKEL, G. S., and GUNN, D. L. *The Orientation of Animals*. Dover Publications, New York, 1961.

FRISCH, K. V. *About Biology*. Oliver & Boyd, Edinburgh, 1962.

GRANIT, R. *Receptors and Sensory Perception*. Yale University Press, New Haven, 1955.

GRIFFIN, D. R. *Listening in the Dark*. Yale University Press, New Haven, 1958.

Handbook of Physiology, Section 'Neurophysiology', Volume 1. American Physiological Society, Washington, D.C., 1959.

HARRISON MATTHEWS, L., and KNIGHT, MAXWELL. *The Senses of Animals*. Museum Press, London, 1963.

HOBBES, T. *Leviathan* (ed. A. D. Lindsay). J. M. Dent & Sons, London, 1957.

HODGKIN, A. L. 'The ionic basis of electrical activity in nerve and muscle'. *Biol. Rev.* **26**, 339–409. Cambridge University Press, 1951.

HODGSON, E. S. 'Taste receptors'. *Scientific American* **204**, 135–44, May 1961.

KATZ, B. 'How cells communicate'. *Scientific American* **205**, 209–20, September 1962.

LAND, E. H. 'Experiments in colour vision'. *Scientific American* **200**, 184–99, May 1959.

LAND, E. H. 'The retinex'. *American Scientist* **52**, 247–64, 1964.

LISSMAN, H. W. 'Electric location in fishes'. *Scientific American* **208**, 50–59, March 1963.

LIVINGSTON, W. K. 'What is pain?'. *Scientific American* **188**, 59–66, March 1953.

LOCKE, J. *An Essay Concerning Human Understanding.* J. M. Dent & Sons, London, 1948.

LOEWENSTEIN, W. R. 'Biological transducers'. *Scientific American* **203**, 98–111, August 1960.

LOWENSTEIN, O. 'Peripheral mechanisms of equilibrium'. *Brit. Med. Bull.* **12**, 114–18, 1956.

LOWENSTEIN, O. 'Comparative physiology of otolith organs'. *Brit. Med. Bull.* **12**, 110–14, 1956.

LOWENSTEIN, O. (ed.). 'A discussion on the ear under water'. *Proc. Roy. Soc. B.* **152**, 1–77, 1959.

LOWENSTEIN, O. (ed.). 'Sensory specialization in response to environmental demands'. *Symp. Zool. Soc. London III.* 1962.

LOWENSTEIN, O. *Lucretius*, Chapter 1 (ed. R. D. Dudley). Routledge & Kegan Paul, London, 1965.

LUCRETIUS *De rerum natura* (English translation by W. H. D. Rouse). William Heinemann, London, 1953.

MILLER, W. H., RATCLIFF, F., and HARTLINE, H. K. 'How cells receive stimuli'. *Scientific American* **205**, 222–83, September 1961.

NICOL, J. A. *The Biology of Marine Animals.* Pitman, London, 1960.

PIRENNE, M. H. 'Light quanta and vision'. *Endeavour* **20**, 197–209, October 1961.

PROSSER, C. L., and BROWN, F. A., Jr. *Comparative animal physiology.* W. B. Saunders Co., New York, 1961.

SCHEER, B. T. *Animal Physiology.* John Wiley, New York, 1963.

SJÖSTRAND, S. F. In *The Structure of the Eye* (ed. G. K. Smelser). Academic Press, New York, 1961.

Symposia of the Society for Experimental Biology, Volume 4, *Physio-*

logical Mechanisms in Animal Behaviour. Cambridge University Press, 1950.

Symposia of the Society for Experimental Biology, Volume 16, *Biological Receptor Mechanisms*. Cambridge University Press, 1962.

WIGGLESWORTH, V. B. *The Life of Insects*. Weidenfeld & Nicolson, London, 1964.

YOUNG, J. Z. *The Life of Vertebrates*. Oxford University Press, 1962.

YOUNG, J. Z. *The Life of Mammals*. Oxford University Press, 1957.

ZOTTERMAN, Y. (ed.). *Olfaction and Taste*. Pergamon Press, Oxford, 1963.

ACKNOWLEDGEMENTS

THE author and publishers wish to acknowledge with thanks permission to reproduce modified redrawings or photo-copies of the following illustrations:

AMOORE, J. E., JOHNSTON, J. W., Jr, and RUBIN, M. 'The stereochemical theory of odor'. *Scientific American* **20**, February 1964, pp. 44 and 45. Copyright Scientific American, New York.

BRETT, J. R. 'The Eye'. In *The Physiology of Fishes* (ed. Margaret Brown), Figure 1, p. 122 (lower part of figure). Academic Press, New York, 1957.

BULLOCK, T. H., and DIECKE, F. P. J. 'Properties of an infra-red receptor'. *J. Physiol.* **134**, 47–87, Figure 1, Plate 1, p. 86. Cambridge University Press, 1956.

DAUMER, K. 'Reizmetrische Untersuchungen des Farbensehens der Bienen'. *Z. vergl. Physiol.* Volume 38, Figure 32, p. 474. Verlag Springer, Berlin.

DETHIER, V. G. 'The physiology and histology of the contact chemoreceptors of the blowfly'. *Quart. Rev. Biol.* **30**, 348–71, Figure 2, p. 350. Messrs Williams & Williams Co., Baltimore, 1955.

DUKE-ELDER, SIR STEWART. *System of Ophthalmology*, Volume 11, Figure 502. Messrs Henry Kimpton, London.

GALAMBOS, R., and DAVIS, H. 'Response of single auditory nerve fibres to acoustic stimulation'. *J. Neurophysiol.* **6**, 39–57, Figure 5, p. 45. American Physiological Society, Washington, 1943.

LANHAM, URL. *The Fishes*, Plate 16. Columbia University Press, New York, 1962.

LISSMAN, H. W. 'Electric location in fishes'. *Scientific American* **208**, March 1963, p. 50, upper figure.

NILSEN, S. E. G. 'Receptor cell outer segment development and ultrastructure of disc membranes in the retina of the Tadpole (*Rana pipiens*)'. *J. Ultrastructure Research*, Volume 11, 581, Figure 15, p. 599. Academic Press, New York, 1964.

*Some other books published by Penguins are
described on the following pages.*

THE PSYCHOLOGY OF HUMAN AGEING

D. B. BROMLEY

Infant and adolescent psychology have been very thoroughly explored: but the study of ageing lags behind.

A gerontologist, who is scientific adviser in this field to the Medical Research Council, fills a gap in the literature of psychology with this new introduction to human ageing and its mental effects. Dealing with the course of life from maturity onwards, Dr Bromley examines many biological and social effects of human ageing; personality and adjustment; mental disorders in adult life and old age; age changes in the organization of occupational and skilled performance; adult intelligence; and age changes in intellectual, social, and other achievements. A final section on method in the study of ageing makes this book an important contribution for the student of psychology as well as the layman.

THE SCIENCE OF ANIMAL BEHAVIOUR

P. L. BROADHURST

For generations men have employed dogs and hawks to hunt, cormorants to fish, and performing animals for entertainment. Modern research, on scientific lines, may enormously widen the use of animals in human society. In this brief and fascinating study the director of London University's animal psychology laboratory recounts how, with the use of test apparatus, monkeys can learn to work for wages paid in token coins; how white rats can be trained to thread their way through a maze or taught specific drills in such devices as the 'shuttle box'. He describes too the scientific observations which have been made on the behaviour of penguins or crabs, for instance, in the wild, and the questions that these raise.

Such experimentation and observation, under approved conditions, can be shown to advance the treatment of human mental disorders and to help the study of such difficult problems as prenatal influences. It might also lead to such extraordinary developments as the training of chimpanzees as engine-drivers or the employment of pigeons as production-line inspectors.

This authoritative book is the only one to explain clearly the meaning and purpose of modern research into animal behaviour.

HUMAN PHYSIOLOGY

KENNETH WALKER

Most of us know too little of the way our bodies work, and are liable in that state of comparative ignorance to become the victims of groundless anxieties about ourselves. In this compact and authoritative survey Kenneth Walker sets forth in plain language the most up-to-date knowledge of the functioning of the human body, and reminds us too how profoundly the mind influences the working of the body.

Starting from the cell, the basis of human as of all life, he describes the nature and work of the digestive, circulatory, excretory, locomotor, and nervous systems: the part that food plays in our lives; how we breathe; the functions of the special senses and the physiology of sensation; the chemistry of the body and the glandular system; and the processes of reproduction. A number of sketches in the text illustrate special points.

'The layman wanting a simple, concise and trustworthy description of the working of the human body need not wish for a better guide than this' – *The Times Literary Supplement*

THE CHEMISTRY OF LIFE

STEVEN ROSE

The molecular structure of a protein (insulin) was described in detail for the first time in 1956: today such procedures are routine. Not only has the pace of biochemistry accelerated in recent years: with the perfection of the electron microscope and the development of cybernetics, the science has also widened and grown more complex.

The Chemistry of Life outlines the scope and achievement of a science which began as the study of the chemical constituents of living matter. Dealing successively with the chemical analysis of the living animal cell, the conversions induced between chemicals by the enzymes acting as catalysts, and the self-regulating nature of cells, Dr Rose explains how the design of particular cells influences their functions within the living organism as a whole.

Biochemistry is a difficult subject. But it is presented here as simply as accuracy will permit by a young research chemist who conveys much of the adventure of discovery implicit in a science which may one day answer the eternal question: 'What is life?'